# THE GOLDEN DAWN SCRAPBOOK

## The Rise and Fall of a Magical Order

R. A. Gilbert

SAMUEL WEISER, INC.

York Beach, Maine

First published in 1997 by
Samuel Weiser, Inc.
P. O. Box 612
York Beach, ME 03910-0612

03  02  01  00  99  98  97
9  8  7  6  5  4  3  2  1

Library of Congress Cataloging-in-Publication Data

Gilbert, R. A.
    Golden Dawn scrapbook : the rise and fall of a magical
order / Robert A. Gilbert.
        p.    cm.
    Includes bibliographical references and index.
    1. Hermetic Order of the Golden Dawn—History. I Title.
BF1623.R7G54    1997
135'.45—DC21                                    97-9600
                                                  CIP

ISBN 1-57863-007-X (hardcover)
ISBN 1-57863-037-1 (paper)

EB

Printed in the United States of America

The paper used in this publication meets the minimum require-
ments of the American National Standard for Permanence of Paper
for Printed Library Materials Z39.48-1984.

# Contents

# Introduction

When I first took up the Hermetic Order of the Golden Dawn 25 years ago, it was decidedly a minority interest. Today it is a very different animal: the dead rituals live again, and the system of esoteric knowledge that underpinned them is taught by a multitude of self-styled adepts to myriads of would-be magicians who rush headlong, like the Gadarene swine, over the cliffs of self-delusion. But it need not be so.

I am not a magician and I have no desire to be a Chief, secret or otherwise, of any magical Order, but I am well aware that the warring bands of magicians who variously claim to be the heirs of the Golden Dawn do not represent its true legacy. There are adepts, possessed of the necessary dedication and integrity to revive the Hermetic Order of the Golden Dawn and restore it to the role intended by its Victorian founders: that of a teaching body that unfolds the psycho-spiritual nature of the Self by way of ceremonial practices based on the symbolism of the Western Mystery Tradition.

Aspiring magicians will not be led to a working temple through the pages of this book; it is not designed to be a manual or practical instruction. Equally, it is not intended to be a documentary history of the Order: that may be found in Ellic Howe's history, *The Magicians of the Golden Dawn* (1972), and, on a more modest scale, in my own *Golden Dawn Companion* (1986).

This book is intended simply to provide an overview of the Order, and to tell its story through the lives and actions (or inactions) of its members. If it seems that I have concentrated on their follies and misdeeds, this is because the story of the Order *is* largely a story of follies and misdeeds.

Recent research into collections of Golden Dawn archives has produced an almost complete prehistory of the Order. In a much abbreviated outline, the story runs like this:

William Wynn Westcott (1848–1925), physician, coroner and magician, listed among his recreations 'Freemasonry' – by which he meant not the mainstream craft, but the many odd Rites and Orders that flourished in late Victorian Britain. Westcott was active in most of them, including the Swedenborgian Rite of Freemasonry, of which Kenneth MacKenzie was the Grand Secretary. When MacKenzie died in 1886, Westcott took up his post and collected from MacKenzie's widow all the papers relevant to the Rite, together with some 'loose papers'. These were nothing other than the Cipher Manuscript.

For Westcott, who, like MacKenzie, had access to Trithemius' *Polygraphiae* (1561) which contained the cipher, translating the Manuscript was easy. And once Westcott knew what he had, he knew also what he would do with it. In Westcott's day, almost every occultist (if a man) was also a freemason and a member of the Masonic Rosicrucian Society, the *Societas Rosicruciana in Anglia*. But that was essentially a study society with a series of simple graded ceremonies and Westcott dreamed of something else. For those who wanted work and not play, there was another society that was, in MacKenzie's words, 'practical and not visionary'. It was, however, severely limited, as its title – The Society of Eight – indicates. Westcott became one of the Eight and thus increased the store of occult knowledge that he would later feed to his budding magicians. He intended MacKenzie's rituals, however, for yet another Order.

The Society of Eight could never grow and, being purely masonic, it could never admit women. To Westcott the admission of women was essential, for by the time he had obtained the Cipher Manuscript he was enraptured by the work of Anna Kingsford, whose Hermetic Society supplied all the theoretical occultism that one could wish for – but without a hint of the practical. There was, however, one avenue still open to him in the form of the Royal Oriental Order of Sikha (Apex) and the Sat B'hai, a quasi-masonic Order supposedly imported

5

from India in 1872 that admitted women to its lower grades. In 1886 it was controlled by John Yarker, the great creator and collector of Rites and Orders, who offered its members a detailed programme of esoteric studies to supplement a set of rather uninspiring rituals.

MacKenzie had long been a member of the Sat B'hai and saw the need to improve the rituals, but his death prevented the completion of his work, the probable outlines of which are contained in the Cipher Manuscript. (Which was enciphered simply to keep it from his wife and his masonic colleagues, none of whom were members of the Order!) The Sat B'hai was inactive to the point of paralysis, but Yarker was very much alive and had no intention of giving it up. Thus in order for Westcott to satisfy his desire to provide a working esoteric Order that offered ritual as well as instruction to both men and women, he must create something entirely new. In March 1888 Westcott finally gave birth to that creation: the Hermetic Order of the Golden Dawn.

Such a brief outline must inevitably leave out much evidence and detail, but I should point out that the evidence presented is not circumstantial but entirely documentary. Those sceptics and cynics who doubt the reality of the archives of the Golden Dawn will find an account of them in the bibliography to this book. Other, more trusting, readers may prefer simply to enjoy the story of the Golden Dawn and its curious members.

# CHAPTER ONE

# 'Religion or Lust?': the Order in the Dock

By October 1901, the Boer War was drawing tortuously to its close; the minor skirmishes to which it had degenerated no longer drew public attention. Newspaper editors in London were anxiously seeking new headlines. What dropped into their laps in the course of that month must thus have seemed nothing short of heaven-sent.

'Religion or Lust?' screamed *The Sun,* easily outdoing *The News of the World*'s 'Sensational Evidence' and *The Daily News*'s 'Hissing the Prisoners'. The event in question was the Committal Proceedings of an American couple, Frank and Editha Jackson, alias Theo and Laura Horos. They had been arrested on 20 September and were charged with conspiring to cheat and defraud a young woman, Vera Croysdale, of both money and jewellery. On 10 October, further charges were laid against them of the alleged 'procurement for immoral purposes' of three young women – Vera Croysdale, Olga Rowson and Daisy Adams. Theo Horos was also charged with the rape of the sixteen-year-old Miss Adams.

To add to the drama, the stories included the contrast between the inadequate Theo and his dominating wife. They were involved in a spurious occult body, The Order of Theocratic Unity, which had been set up by the couple. Laura Horos was known in the organisation as 'The Swami Viva Ananda'. For two months a prurient public was regaled with lurid accounts of the misdoings of the pair and their 'revolting and abominable conduct', in the words of the bench. These accounts were repeated during their trial in December at the

POLICE·BUDGET·EDITION EDITED·BY·HAROLD·FURNISS

FAMOUS **CRIMES**

PAST·AND·PRESENT ONE·PENNY

THE SWAMI.

Vol. VIII. No. 108.  (A Sketch of Madame Horos at the Old Bailey.)

*Laura Horos (alias The Swami Viva Ananda, Mrs Diss Debar and Angel Anna) as seen by a staff artist of* Famous Crimes, *at the time of her trial in 1901 for swindling and for aiding and abetting rape by her husband Frank Jackson (alias Theo Horos). Her colourful life had a prosaic beginning. She was born Editha Salomon in Harrodsburg, Kentucky, 1849.*

Central Criminal Court. Both were found guilty and both were gaoled, Theo Horos for 15 years and The Swami for seven. But while most members of the public had revelled in the histrionics and extraordinary dress of the gross and flamboyant Swami who conducted her own defence, there were others who had viewed the proceedings with dismay and alarm.

On 11 October, under the heading 'The Order of the Golden Dawn. Miss Croysdale tells the story of how she was duped', the *Evening News* began its report on the Horos Case with the text of the Obligation that Vera Croysdale had been persuaded to sign before she had been admitted to the Theocratic Unity. It read as follows:

> I, Vera Croysdale, in the presence of the Lord of the Universe and in the Hall of the Neophytes of the Order of the G.D. in the Outer, regularly assembled under Warrant from the G.H. Chiefs of the Second Order, do of my own free will and

*The Swami's court appearances were dramatic. Between October and December 1901 the public flocked to the committal proceedings at Marylebone Police Court and to the trial at the Central Criminal Court – partly to listen to Madame Horos conduct her own defence. They expected a theatrical performance and were not disappointed.*

accord hereby and hereon most solemnly pledge myself to keep secret this Order, its name, the names of its members, and the proceedings which take place at its meetings, from all and every person in the whole world, who is outside the pale of the Order, and not even to discuss these with initiates, unless he or they are in possession of the password for the time being, nor yet with any member who has resigned, demitted, or been expelled; and I undertake to maintain a kindly and benevolent relation with all the Fratres and Sorores of the Order.

I furthermore promise and swear that I will keep secret any information relating to this Order which may have become known to me prior to the completion of the ceremony of my admission; and I also pledge myself to divulge nothing whatsoever concerning this Order to the outside world, in case either of my resignation, demission or expulsion. I will not seek to obtain any writings or ritual pertaining to the Order of the G.D. in the Outer without due authorisation

THEO HYPNOTISES HIS VICTIM.

*Theo Horos was unquestionably guilty as charged, and presented as such by the press, and did not help his case by conducting his own defence – in a most inept manner. At one point during the committal proceedings he turned to the public gallery (from where he was being hissed) and shouted out, 'Keep quiet, you reptiles!' What became of him after his 15 years in prison is not recorded.*

from the praemonstrator of my Temple; nor will I possess any letter or lecture unless it be properly registered and labelled by him.

I further undertake that any such ritual or lecture and any case, cover, or box containing them, shall bear the official label of the G.D. I will not copy myself, nor lend to any other person to be copied, any ritual or paper until and unless I hold the written permission of the praemonstrator so to do, lest the secret knowledge be revealed and that through my neglect or error.

Furthermore I undertake to prosecute with zeal the study of the occult sciences, seeing that this Order is not established for the benefit of those who desire only a superficial knowledge hereof. I will not suffer myself to be hypnotised or mesmerised, nor will I place myself in such a passive state that any uninitiated person, power or being may cause me to lose the control of my thoughts, words or actions; neither will I use my occult knowledge for evil purposes. And I further promise to persevere with firmness and courage through the ceremonies and studies as far as is humanly possible.

All these points I generally and severally, upon this sacred and sublime symbol, swear to observe without evasion, equivocation, or mental reservation of any kind whatsoever, under the no less penalty on the violation of any or either of them than that of being expelled from this Order as a wilfully-perjured wretch, void of all moral worth, and unfit for the society of all upright and true persons, and, in addition, under the awful penalty of voluntarily submitting myself to a deadly and hostile current of will, set in motion by the chiefs of the Order, by which I should fall slain or paralysed without visible weapon, as if blasted by the lightning flash.

Sacred seal and signature,

Vera Croysdale

So help me, the Lord of the Universe and my own higher soul.

After this text had been read out in Court, Miss Croysdale described her initiation, which *The Daily News* reported verbatim: 'She was first blindfolded and had a rope tied round her waist. Then she was led into another room, and somebody said: "Child of Earth, I consecrate thee with Water. Child of Earth, I consecrate thee with Fire". "I heard Madame and her husband moving about the room", she continued, "but, of course, I could not see anything. The reason I can tell you so clearly what happened is because after my initiation I helped in the initiation of other neophytes."

Then I had to kneel down and place my right hand on the Sign of the Red Cross. I had to grasp the hand of the male prisoner, and he said a kind of prayer over me – which I had to repeat. Then I repeated the Obligation over again. They used both fire and water. When I was consecrated with water, the man made a cross on my forehead with his wet finger. For the fire ceremony, I had to hold my hands over a kind of lamp. There was a sword used. I'm not quite sure what was done with it early in the ceremony, but at the end it was sheathed over my head. After that I had to partake of bread and salt, and then a rose was passed round.

'The man, she added, subsequently made to her the impious suggestion that he was Christ Himself, and "the only perfect man in the world". He also told her that sin committed with him would be an act of piety, and that offspring born as the result of their intimacy would be Divine. During the next few days she was repeatedly hypnotised by one or other of the prisoners and she was regularly drugged every morning with a concoction of milk, eggs, whisky, and some other ingredient.'

Where this extraordinary ritual had come from soon became clear. Inspector John Kane, who had arrested them at Birkenhead, told the court that he had 'taken possession of a deed box, portmanteau and bag, all belonging to the prisoners; also other similar boxes and travelling trunks', amongst which he found 'a number of books containing the ritual of the "Golden Dawn"'. Those books appeared to have belonged to a Mr Mathers. They showed that there was more than one obligation – an opening and a justification – which corresponded with the ritual of the Theocratic Unity. In fact the ritual of that Order corresponded exactly with the ritual of the Theocratic Unity, the titles used – Hierophant and Hiereus – being also identical. In a printed book he found a number of symbols said to be connected with the Order of the Golden Dawn. Furthermore, some items of the regalia used in the rituals of the Theocratic Unity 'were similar to those used in the Order of the Golden Dawn in Paris'. He added that 'there was such an order as the "Golden Dawn" the principal of which was Macgregor Mathers. The witness believed it to be a perfectly pure order. It was distinguished by absolutely none of the incidents that had been mentioned in this case' and that Macgregor Mathers was 'a man of the highest possible character'. Not surprisingly, the Swami disagreed. 'He is,' she said, 'a traitor – a sworn enemy of the British Empire. He dares not show himself on English soil.' She also said that Mathers' book, *The Key of Solomon the King*, was 'black magic'.

Unfortunately for Mathers the disclaimers of Inspector Kane were lost among the more sensational aspects of the case. His letter to the magistrate, setting out the true state of affairs between the Horos pair and the Golden Dawn was not read out in court. An altered version of this letter was printed in the journal *Light* after the trial had ended, but it lacked the impact of the original:

28 Rue Saint Vincent,
Paris – Oct. 13. 1901

To Curtis Bennett Esq. Magistrate, Marylebone Police Court, W.C.

Sir,

Re case of Horos and Order of the G.D.

I am and have been for years the Head of the above Order, and I write to protest against the shameful and unauthorised abuse of its name by Mr and Mrs Horos for their own immoral purposes.

It is an association for the study of the Archaeology of Mysticism and the origin and application of Religious and Occult Symbolism. Its teachings are *strictly moral* and inculcate a profound respect for the truths of all Religions. It has members all over the world, many of them of the highest social and intellectual rank, and of moral standing. The *real* name of the Order has been from ancient time kept secret to prevent, as far as possible, impostors and adventurers from making use of its name to shield their malpractices; as has been frequently done by unscrupulous persons with respect to other associations, the Jesuit Order for example.

Thus then the words 'the Order of the Golden Dawn' is only a way of translating the letters G.D.

I being the Head of this Order no meeting of its Members is official without my consent and authority, and to such persons as the prisoners my consent and authorisation never has been, and never would be given.

13

These individuals, accompanied by Mrs Rose Adams, calling herself Doctor of Medicine, came to me in Paris in the beginning of last year, professing to be interested in Egyptological research and to be Members of my Order in America, and also of the Theosophical Society. On the strength of this Mrs Horos managed to obtain possession of several manuscripts of the Order of the G.D.; from which they have evidently concocted some garbled form of initiation to impose upon their unfortunate victims. I have vainly tried since to make them return these manuscripts and other articles they had borrowed from me. It did not take me long to find out what kind of persons the prisoners are; and I refused to receive them. Among other peculiar statements which Mrs Horos made, and which first aroused my suspicions as these persons had come to me with a good introduction, were:-

'That Mrs Annie Besant had gone mad, and that they had come to Europe to supplant her as Head of the Theosophical Society.'

'That Mrs Horos was the illegitimate daughter of Pope Pius the Ninth and Lola Montes.'

'That she had been admitted as a 'courte-robe' of the Jesuit fraternity, and had the support of the influence of that Order which she could bring to bear to break up any association she pleased, and she menaced the Order of the G.D. herewith, against which she said "that they had already directed some of their force."'

'That Mrs Horos was identical with the Diana Vaughan of Leon Taxil notoriety.'

It was these and other statements and threats, coupled with their evidently immoral ideas which made me refuse to receive them.

I most emphatically deny that their 'Theocratic Unity' has anything whatsoever to do with the G.D., & in justice to this Order, I should be grateful to you to make known the fact.

Yours faithfully,

MacGregor

*Mathers' claim that he had known the Horoses to be frauds rings hollow when an entry in the Minute Book of the Abathoor Temple for 16 February 1900 is read, in which he proposed three new members: Theo Horos, Laura Horos and Rose Adams, identified here by their Latin mottoes. His proposal was adopted unanimously.*

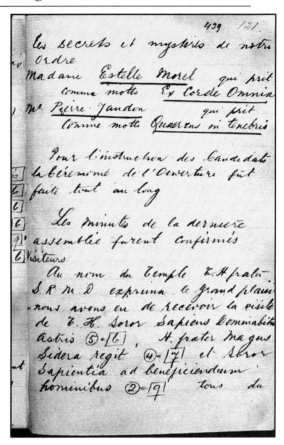

(In the version sent to *Light* he signed himself in full: 'S.L. MacGregor Mathers, Comte MacGregor de Glenstrae')

That the Golden Dawn and the Theocratic Unity were not one and the same was made clear in court, but the public was inclined to ridicule the whole notion of occult orders and poked fun at the Golden Dawn especially. Most members of the Order, believing discretion to be the better part of valour, 'laid low and said nuthin', particularly because they knew that Mathers' letter was less than truthful. By 1901 he was head of only a small part of the Golden Dawn, and far from being suspicious of the Horoses he had been utterly taken in by them.

In January of 1900 Theo and the Swami had met Mathers in Paris and convinced him not only that they were members of the American Thoth Hermes Temple, but that the Swami was none other than Anna Sprengel, the mysterious (and mythical) adept by whose fiat the Golden Dawn had come into being. Mathers invited them and the equally dubious Rose Adams to a meeting of his Ahathoor Temple. It was duly recorded in the Minute Book on 16 February that they witnessed the Neophyte ceremony and were received in a manner befitting their apparent rank:

> In the name of the Temple V.H. Frater S.R.M.D. [S'Rioghail Mo Dhream – Mathers' motto in the Order] expressed the great pleasure we feel in receiving the visit of V.H. Soror Sapiens Dominabitur Astris 5 = 6 [Mme Horos], H. Frater Magus Sidera regit 4 = 7 [Theo Horos] and Soror Sapientia ad beneficiendum hominibus 2 = 9 [Rose Adams] all of TH(oth) (Her)mes Temple No. 8. He proposed that as these sorores and frater would be staying in Paris for a year, they should be elected honorary members of our Temple. This proposition was seconded by V.H. Soror V.N.R. [Vestigia Nulla Retrorsum – Mrs Mathers] and V.H. Frater Ex Animo [Robert Nisbet] and adopted nem. con.

Far from appreciating the honour, Theo and the Swami used the opportunity to purloin the Neophyte ritual and other documents. They then decamped to South Africa, returning to England in November. Here they met other members of the Golden Dawn who had thrown off Mathers' yoke and were less impressed by the couple. Dr Westcott declined an interview with Theo who wished to discuss 'the subject of the Hermetic Society' and sent him on to F.L. Gardner and Percy Bullock, both of whom were senior members of long standing. They were suspicious of 'Mr Cornish', as Theo introduced himself to them. They sent him packing when he claimed to be a member of a non-existent Thema Temple in India, with the words, 'We know all about you'. The Swami was not with him on this occasion because she was 'too corpulent to climb four flights of stairs'.

Mathers had of course become aware of his mistake as soon as he realised that his manuscripts had been stolen. He promptly warned his former colleagues in London. In defence of his gullibility, he told Aleister Crowley that he was 'pitifully in distress at having been fooled', and that Mrs Horos was able to repeat to him a certain conversation he had had years previously when he visited Madame Blavatsky at Denmark Hill. The repetition of this scrap of conversation had convinced him of her status.

But once the trial was out of the way, members of the Golden Dawn who were loyal to Mathers attempted to salvage the Order's reputation, but succeeded only in besmirching it further. Dr Edward Berridge, who was known as 'Resurgam' in the Order, wrote to the journal *Light* in the wake of Mathers' letter:

> I have been asked why the Horoses were not punished by occult means. *They were so punished.* For a considerable time they had carried on their nefarious career with comparative impunity: when, however, they defrauded the Order by misrepresentations and treachery, and attempted to destroy it, the terrible vengeance of the Secret Chiefs fell upon them.
>
> It was necessary, in the interests of society, that their guilt should be openly revealed and punished. Had an occult current then been sent against them, it would have only caused them to exchange the well-merited living death of penal servitude for the comforts of the penal infirmary; and had they been slain by the same means, they would have become dangerous entities on the astral plane and, by obsessing some unfortunate medium, have wrought incalculable harm.
>
> The detective who brought me the stolen property of the Order and its Chief, which I have now returned to the latter, informed me that the woman boasted that she would hypnotise the jury. The newspapers recorded that before each appearance in Court she seemed engaged in silent prayer. No prayer would have emanated from either of the miscreants, unless it was a prayer to Satan! She was really endeavouring to hypnotise her judges and accusers, and also to surround herself with an occult defence against the righteous punitive current which she feared would be sent against her. But it was of no avail.

17

Her hypnotic devices were perceived by the Chiefs, and a current was sent against her more than once; and resulted in the sudden attacks of illness, of the nature of incipient paralysis, which the newspapers recorded; and it also destroyed her hypnotic power.

The facts of occult science are stern and terrible realities; and all treachery is severely punished in some way or other. Perhaps there will be a further illustration of this in the case of other enemies of the order.

Resurgam, Fra. R.R. et A.C.

(Cancellarius of the Isis-Urania Temple, of the (real) Order of the G D)

The minatory reference to 'enemies of the Order' was inspired by Mathers' own letter which had described 'certain dissensions in my Order, stirred up by a few members, constant fomenters of discord, jealous of my authority, though clamorous for my teaching'. Mathers implied that these 'fomenters of discord' had sent Mr and Mrs Horos to him. He added that the presence of the Horoses coincided with dissension in the Order which resulted in several of the members leaving.

The inconsistencies in Berridge's bombastic and intemperate letter were apparent to the readers of *Light*. It evoked a sardonic response from a reader who wrote using the pseudonym of Vérité Sans Peur, protesting against Berridge's 'boasting occult powers'. The anonymous writer commented that Berridge's letter implied:

That the Chiefs of this terrible Order are possessed of: 1. Clairvoyant powers of a very advanced quality; 2. They must have a gift of prevision; 3. They must have a knowledge of the powers of nature called Occult, and be able to put them into practice by producing results on the material plane; 4. They must have power over *life and death*.

Vérité Sans Peur went on, however, to deride these claims:

Now what does Mr MacGregor Mathers say? In his letter in *Light* of January 11th, he declares that he *is*, and has been for years, the Head of the Order of G D; and its teachings, he says, are of the highest social and religious virtues, and fraternal charity, and those persons who cannot adhere to these principles are *neither allowed to come in* nor to *remain members.* He points out, moreover, that dissension is rife in the Order, that the Horoses presented themselves and deceived him most cruelly by pretending to be members of his Order; that he does not know how they became possessed of the knowledge; that Mrs Horos *managed to take from his house* certain MSS. relating to the Order which she promised to return, but he had not yet succeeded *in getting them back.* The words 'my Order' are used six times in his letter, but no secret Chiefs are mentioned, he being the Head.

If the Head or Chiefs of this Order have the clairvoyant faculty, why was it not used when the dissentients presented themselves for admission? All this internal discord would then have been avoided. And when the Horoses presented themselves, why did these rulers permit themselves to be deceived and allow secret MSS. to be stolen, and in part ultimately published, and the letters G D used with the name Horos? Was the implied prevision of any service to this Head, or to the Chiefs or Rulers, when such stupendous troubles could have been averted? What use is this punitive current of will when it cannot command the return of MSS., protect its Chiefs and members from disgraceful slander, nay more, protect the name of the Order and its ritual?

All this talk about occult powers, astral plane, astral projection, astral existence, is most misleading, and this assumption of knowledge a dangerous deception; and it brings odium upon a most interesting branch of transcendental philosophy. What right has 'Resurgam' to say that had these Horoses been slain they would have become 'dangerous entities on the astral plane'? How can he know? To frighten and deceive weak-minded students who are honest and true in their studies, with these threats of occult powers is, to my mind, a most unwarranted pretence.

Vérité Sans Peur concluded the critique by roundly condemning 'occult powers': 'There is no ground for belief in the existence of such a power, and if there were, its use would deserve to be denounced as malignant, cruel and revolting'.

Vérité Sans Peur might also have denounced the moral laxity of the Secret Chiefs who permitted the Horoses to commit far worse offences with impunity for some 18 months after the theft of the manuscripts.

Berridge, however, firmly believed in occult powers and ended this correspondence with an abusive rejoinder that derided 'weak-minded students', effectively likened Mathers to Christ, and defied rational answer. Here the matter rested. But for many there remained tantalising and unanswered questions: What *was* the Order of the Golden Dawn? From where did it spring? Who were its members? And, above all, just *what* did they do? The more perceptive enquirers might have come across odd clues in print from ten years before, but they would never have uncovered the true story.

# CHAPTER TWO

# Order out of Chaos: the Birth of the Golden Dawn

W e shall never know the precise date on which The Hermetic Order of the Golden Dawn was conceived in the minds of its founders, but it crept into the real world on 12 February, 1888, some 13 years before the trial of the Horoses, when its creator (Dr William Wynn Westcott) and his cronies (Dr William Robert Woodman and Samuel Liddell Mathers) signed their pledges of undying allegiance to themselves. This first official document of the fledgling Order is nothing if not uninspiring:

### Order of the G.D.

For the purpose of the study of Occult Science, and the further investigation of the Mysteries of Life and Death, and our Environment, permission has been granted by the Secret Chiefs of the R.C. to certain Fratres learned in the Occult Sciences, (and who are also members of the Soc. Ros. in Ang.) to work the Esoteric Order of the G.D. in the Outer; to hold meetings thereof for Study and to initiate any approved person *Male* or *Female*, who will enter into an Undertaking to maintain strict secrecy regarding all that concerns it. Belief in One God necessary. No other restrictions.

N.B. This Order is *not* established for the benefit of those who desire only a superficial knowledge of Occult Science.

*Preliminary Pledge to be signed by Intending Candidate*

I the undersigned do hereby solemnly pledge myself:

(1) That I am above the age of 21 years.

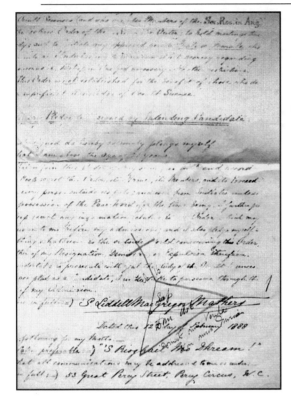

*The first style of Pledge Form used in the Golden Dawn. This is a copy of Mathers' own pledge signed by him on 12 February 1888, countersigned by Anna Sprengel (Sap. Dom. Ast.), Woodman (Vincit Omnia Veritas) and Westcott (Non Omnis Moriar).*

(2) That I join this Order of my own free will and accord.

(3) To keep secret this Order, its Name, its Members, and its Proceedings, from every person outside its pale; and even from Initiates unless in actual possession of the Pass-Word for the time being. I further promise to keep secret any information relative to this Order which may become known to me before my admission; and I also pledge myself to divulge nothing whatsoever to the outside World concerning this Order in case either of my Resignation, Demission, or Expulsion therefrom.

(4) I undertake to prosecute with zeal the study of the Occult Sciences.

(5) If accepted as a Candidate, I undertake to persevere through the Ceremony of my Admission.

To this the aspiring member appended his or her full name and address, together with the motto selected for use within the Order, this being preferably in Latin, and the date.

There is nothing in the Order's recorded history to suggest a sudden influx either of pagans or of weak-minded spiritualist mediums, but the Pledge Form was soon altered to include the following restrictions:

> **Belief in a Supreme Being, or Beings, is indispensable. In addition, the Candidate, if not a Christian, should be at least prepared to take an interest in Christian symbolism.**

> **The Chiefs of the Order do not care to accept as Candidates any persons accustomed to submit themselves as Mediums to the Experiments of Hypnotism, Mesmerism, or Spiritualism; or who habitually allow themselves to fall into a completely passive condition of Will; also they disapprove of the methods made use of as a rule in such Experiments.**

From all of this it is clear what the Order stood for, but not the manner in which it was propagated. It was an avowedly Secret Society, analogous in the popular view to Freemasonry but with the added attraction that it took in both men and women. The Golden Dawn appealed to esoterically-minded freemasons, most of whom were already members of the Societas Rosicruciana in Anglia, the one extant Rosicrucian body. It had been founded in 1867 and demanded (as it still does) a masonic qualification for membership. The Order also appealed to members of the Theosophical Society who were disenchanted with the eastern bias of the Society's teachings and with the alleged trickery that was uncovered at Adyar in 1885 during the investigation by the Society for Psychical Research. Presumably the earliest members all learned initially of the Golden Dawn by word of mouth, for some 60 men and women had joined the Order before the first guarded announcement of its existence appeared in print on 9 February, 1889.

Replying to an earlier question in *Notes and Queries* about a 'Society of Kabbalists', a question almost certainly sent in by himself, Dr Westcott gave to the world the following mixture of fact and fancy:

> The order of mystics which gave Eliphaz Lévi (Abbé
> Constant), his occult knowledge, and of which Johann Falk
> was at one time the Lecturer on the Kabbalah in London, is
> still at work in England. It is not a Masonic Order, and there
> is no distinction between men and women students. The
> greatest privacy is maintained, and some knowledge of
> Hebrew is essential, but the whole course of study and
> experiment is so abstruse and complex that the membership
> is very limited as to numbers, and the proceedings have no
> public interest. Its true name is only told to initiates, and the
> few outsiders who have heard of its existence only know the
> society as 'The Hermetic Students of the G.D'.
>
> Wm. Wynn Westcott, M.B.
>
> 396 Camden Road, London, N.

New members – some of whom may have been drawn in as
a result of this portentous 'Note' – went through the Neophyte
Ceremony, signed the Obligation (the wording of which was
made public during the Horos trial) and were given the traditional History of the Order:

> Some years have passed away since it was decided to revive
> the Order of the G.D. in the Outer, an Hermetic Society
> whose members are taught the principles of Occult Science,
> and the practice of the Magic of Hermes; the decease during
> the second half of the century of several eminent adepts and
> chiefs of the Order, having caused a temporary dormant
> condition. Prominent among these Adepts was Eliphaz Lévi,
> the greatest of modern French Magi, Ragon, the author of
> several classical books on occult subjects; Kenneth
> Mackenzie, author of the Masonic Encyclopaedia, and
> Frederick Hockley, famous for his crystal seeing and his MSS.
> These and other contemporary adepts received their
> knowledge and power from predecessors of equal and of
> greater eminence but of even more concealed existence.

The History went on to explain how the rituals of the
revived Order had been built up from a series of manuscripts in
cipher which had been given to Westcott 'some years before by
a most eminent and illuminated Hermetist (since dead) whose

title was Frater "Vive Momor Lethi". He had been for many years in communication with prominent British and Foreign Adepts, and he had enjoyed ample access to the writing of Eliphaz Lévi. This collection of MSS has since been supplemented by a varied collection of MSS chiefly in cipher which have been either given or lent to the Chiefs of the temple by our Continental Fratres and Sorores.' In practical terms, 'These MSS provided the Adepts who possessed the secret of their occult meaning, with the ability to extend the order of the G.D. in the Outer subject to the approval of the Chiefs of the Second Order'.

These adepts to which the History referred were, of course, Westcott, Woodman and Mathers, who obtained the necessary approval 'from the G.H. Soror "Sap: Dom. Ast" in Germany' and were 'duly instructed to extend the Order in England, and this Temple was consecrated as a successor to Hermanubis No. 2 which had ceased to exist, owing to the decease of all its Chiefs'.

The 'Historical Lecture' contains much more than this, but these are all the significant features of the story: the cipher manuscripts in the hands of earlier adepts; the suppositious Hermanubis Temple; and the authority of mysterious German adepts – although the question of just how Westcott had come by the manuscripts and what led him to 'Soror Sapiens Dominabitur Astris' (issues neatly avoided in the lecture) – has been the subject of much fruitless speculation. When pressed Westcott displayed a copy of a letter allegedly written by the Revd. A.F.A. Woodford, Frater Vive Momor Lethi of the Historical Lecture, and a prominent masonic scholar, together with a copy of a note supposedly found 'with A.F.A. Woodford's MSS' and a further '*Note of a conversation with A.F.A.W.* Feb. 1886', all three being in Westcott's own hand.

In the *Note of a conversation with A.F.A.W.,* Woodford claimed to possess 'some real Rosic. MSS. in cipher, a whole series of degrees'. Woodford suggested to Westcott that, 'Some day, I may give them away or perhaps to you. I cannot use them. The Cipher translates into English, yet they came to me from a correspondent in France with a history that they had passed through Lévi's hands and indeed a loose page among them has a note signed A.L.C.' In time he did give the manuscripts to Westcott, sending with them this extraordinary letter:

6 Liston Road, Grafton Square

Clapham Road. 8 August, 1887

Dear Br. Westcott,

With this I send MSS. under seal, which I promised, in cipher. It confers upon the possessor who understands the meaning to grant the old Rosicrucian secrets and the grades of Hēoōs chrusē; or Golden Dawn. Try to see old Soror 'Sapiens dominabitur astris' in Germany. She did live at Ulm. Hockley now being dead I know of no one else who could help you.

Yours sincerely

A.F.A. Woodford

Extraordinary, because the note found with the manuscripts (and itself in cipher) identifies the 'old Soror' and provides her accommodation address. The manuscripts contain nothing which suggests they are any kind of warrant to confer grades or degrees, Rosicrucian or otherwise. The note simply says (in Westcott's translation):

'Sapiens dominabitur astris' is a chief among the members of 'Die Goldene Dammerung' and is a famous member of the Order. The name is Fr. A. Sprengel letters may be addressed to
Herr J Enger
Hotel Marquardt
Stuttgart

The cipher text adds her grade, 7 = 4, but omits her initial 'A' – with the implication that Westcott's 'copy' (which he dates as 'supposed 1866') was translated into the cipher rather than out of it.

Whatever the wanderings of this particular manuscript, Westcott did write to Fraulein Sprengel, having the letters translated into German and her replies put into English by a Mr

*The second letter to Westcott from Anna Sprengel.*

Albert Essinger of the Sanitary Wood Wool Company, a firm in which he had a financial stake. Ten years later, when Mathers was beginning to cast doubts on Westcott's integrity, Essinger signed an affidavit concerning his translations, but it proves nothing as it has no bearing on the source of the letters. The letters, however, do exist, and from the beginning Anna Sprengel gave Westcott and his companions full authority while abdicating from any responsibility:

Recd 26 Nov. 1887

Dear Brother,

I have long left the address to which you sent a letter but it has safely reached me at last. I am very glad to hear that the private papers which you describe have been found once more, they were lost by poor Abbé Constant years ago and then came into the hands of two Englishmen who applied for leave to use them. The Temple of Hermanubis was granted to them, but I never heard that anything useful had happened.

As you have succeeded in understanding them I do by my

*Westcott's own translation of the second letter from Anna Sprengel (January 1888).*

power raise you to the 7 = 4 of the Second Order in England, the l'aube dorée of France and Die goldene Dammerung of the German nation.

Begin a new Temple No. 3 and choose two learned persons to form the first three chiefs; when you have raised three more adepts to 5 = 6 you may be independent.

Hermetic science languishes in our time, we are but very few even here, but are very earnest and possess much power, but we mistrust posts and letters, so cannot help you or tell you very much. Write to me under cover of the Sec. of the Lodge Licht Liebe Leben which address you know.

I remain,

Sap. Dom. Ast. 7 = 4

**Frater 'In Utroque Fidelis' often writes my letters for me.**

(This is from an English translation in Westcott's hand – it differs in many minor details from a strict translation of the German original.)

Over the course of the next two years Westcott received a further four letters – authorising him to sign Fraulein Sprengel's motto on her behalf; sending him further manuscripts so that adept degrees could be worked; praising him for his progress; and giving the three Chiefs independent authority, together with a certificate officially conferring the Degree of 7 = 4 Adeptus Exemptus on the Chiefs and permitting them to work degrees up to 6 = 5 (Adeptus Major). The last letter from Germany was not from Soror S.D.A. but from Frater ex Uno Disces Omnes, who wrote on 23 August, 1890, to tell Westcott that Anna Sprengel was dead and that the other German adepts had not approved the founding of Isis Urania; and that they would neither write again nor give further assistance. But by this time two further temples had been founded and the Golden Dawn was in full working order. Anna Sprengel had indeed served Westcott well.

There was much however about both the letters and the cipher manuscripts that was highly suspicious, and they would eventually prove to be a millstone around Westcott's neck.

The cipher manuscripts, which masked a text wholly in English, were written in brown ink on sheets of old paper with a watermark of 1809, but the presence of expressions borrowed from the *Egyptian Book of the Dead* and of Tarot Trump attributions taken from Eliphas Lévi's *Dogme et Rituel de l'Haute Magie* rules out any possibility that the text is earlier than 1870 and places it closer to 1880. Eliphas Lévi himself is thus most unlikely to have owned, or even to have seen Westcott's manuscripts and both Fraulein Sprengel and the Revd. Woodford were evidently misinformed – or, if one is inclined to be cynical, Westcott was not careful enough in concocting the manuscript's history. It would, of course, demand a much higher degree of cynicism to suggest any significance in the facts that by 1874 Westcott owned a copy of Lévi's *Dogme et Rituel* and that by 1887 he was fully conversant with Egyptian funerary texts, as is clear from the text of his book *The Isiac Tablet.*

Doubts about the Sprengel letters and the cipher manuscripts did eventually arise among the Order members, but these were not expressed until 1900 when Mathers, in a typically intemperate letter and displaying a quality of judgement which can be gauged by the fact that he wrote it on the same day – February 16 – that he made the Horoses honorary members of the Ahathoor Temple, informed Florence Farr that Westcott:

> has NEVER been *at any time* either in personal or in written
> communication with the Secret Chiefs of the Order, he
> having *either himself forged or procured to be forged* the
> professed correspondence between him and them, and my
> tongue having been tied all these years by a previous Oath of
> Secrecy to him, demanded by him, from me, before showing
> me what he had either done or caused to be done or both.
> You must comprehend from what little I say here, the
> *extreme gravity* of such a matter, and again I ask you, both
> for his sake and that of the Order, not to force me to go
> further into the subject.

The consequences of this letter were, as we shall see, dramatic in the extreme. It did, after all, sound the death-knell of the old Order. But Mathers cast no doubt upon the cipher manuscripts, for if he had done, it would have destroyed the validity of the whole system. Indeed, at the time of this dénounement other members were also anxious to defend the legitimacy of their rituals, but in later years they became more dispassionate and some of their comments were nothing if not harsh. In 1916 R.W. Felkin, who headed the Stella Matutina faction and who was predisposed to believe in Secret Chiefs, ancient rituals and anything else that came the way of his psychic vision, told A.E. Waite that 'Sapere Aude [Westcott] had put all the Egyptian references into the Cipher MSS. whereas S.A. told me that he had

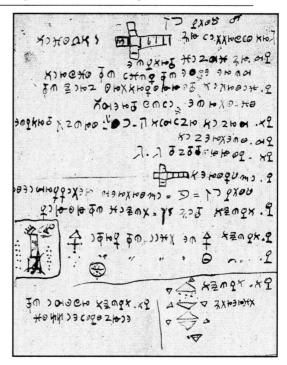

*Folio 48 from the cipher manuscript, containing a part of the 4 = 7 Philosophus ceremony.*

only corrected them'. By 1938, when he published his autobiography, Waite himself thought that 'the G D Ritual Notes were produced well after 1870 – perhaps even ten years later', but he has also maintained 'that they were not the work of Westcott, Woodman and Mathers'. Elsewhere he implied that Kenneth Mackenzie may have owned and produced the cipher manuscripts. Like many of his fellows Waite retained an affection for Westcott and was unwilling to condemn him utterly.

A similar reticence is apparent in the comments of Arthur Machen, who gave no names for the 'originators' of the Golden Dawn and who made it quite clear that he had enjoyed the Order's pretensions even if it 'shed no ray of any kind on my path':

> The Twilight Star [The Golden Dawn] was a stumer – or stumed – to use a very old English word. Its true date of origin was 1880–1885 at earliest. The 'Cipher Manuscript' was written on paper that bore the watermark of 1809 in ink

31

that had a faded appearance. But it contained information that was not known to any living being until twenty years later. It was, no doubt, a forgery of the early eighties. Its originators must have had some knowledge of Freemasonry; but, so ingeniously was this occult fraud 'put upon the market' that, to the best of my belief, the flotation remains a mystery to this day. But what an entertaining mystery; and, after all, it did nobody any harm.

The kindest comments on the Golden Dawn manuscripts were those of W.B. Yeats in the Notes to his *Autobiographies* (1926). 'The foundation of this society,' he wrote,

> which took place some forty years ago, remains almost as obscure as that of some ancient religion. I am sorry to have shed so little light upon a matter which has importance, because in several countries men who have come into possession of its rituals claim, without offering proof, authority from German or Austrian Rosicrucians. I add, however, that I am confident from internal evidence that the rituals, as I knew them, were in substance ancient though never so in language unless some ancient text was incorporated. There was a little that I thought obvious and melodramatic, and it was precisely in this little I am told, that they resembled Masonic rituals, but much that I thought beautiful and profound.

Nonetheless, he tempered his praise with mature judgement:

> I do not know what I would think if I were to hear them now for the first time, for I cannot judge what moved me in my youth.

And youth had been the keynote of the Order. Westcott was 40 when he gave translations of the cipher texts to the 33-year-old Mathers to build them up into complete rituals. Woodman, it is true, was 60 in 1888 and many of the earliest members who had slipped in from the S.R.I.A. had long ago slipped out of their youth, but Mrs. Mathers – then Mina Bergson – was only 22 when she became the first member to

*Westcott's original translation of the first leaf of the cipher manuscript.*

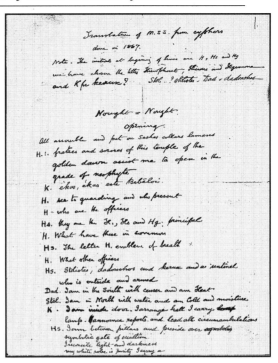

follow the three Chiefs into Isis-Urania. It was her youth, and that of others like her whose enthusiasm was unbounded, that gave the Order its vitality and ensured that when the Tower of Babel they erected on Westcott's shifting foundations finally collapsed, there would be a magnificence about the ruins.

Yeats was surely right to recall the Order in such terms. When he dedicated *A Vision* to Mina, as 'Vestigia Nulla Retrorsum', her motto in the Golden Dawn, he suggested that

> 'Perhaps this book has been written because a number of young men and women, you and I among the number, met nearly forty years ago in London and Paris to discuss mystical philosophy. You with your beauty and your learning and your mysterious gifts were held by all in affection.' But the tower had fallen, and 'much had happened since we copied the Jewish Schemahamphorasch with its seventy-two Names of God in Hebrew characters . . . All other students who were once friends or friends' friends were dead or estranged.'

What was it that brought the Order down? After a decade of continuing growth, and of a membership whose aspirations had no seeming limit, the energy faded, enthusiasm waned and confusion and indifference took their place. A curious malaise had set in, but it was due to no inherent sickness in the Order itself – rather it had its roots in those very members whose activity had built it up. A magical Order is by its nature hierarchical and demanding of obedience, but the nature of the magician is to command rather than to obey. Had there been any with eyes to see – alas, there were none – rebellion and warfare would have been foreseen: self-destruction was the Order's inevitable fate.

# From Foundation to the Abyss: The Rise and Fall of the Order

Soror Sapiens Dominabitur Astris had granted Westcott the right to found his 'new society' in November 1887. Within three months he and his fellow Chiefs had signed the Pledge Form of the 'Esoteric Order of the G.D. in the Outer' and on 1 March, 1888, they had issued a Warrant, with all the authority of Chiefs of the Second Order, to their own alter egos of 'S'Rioghail Mo Dhream' (Mathers); 'Quod Scis Nescis' (Westcott); and 'Magna est Veritas et Praevalebit' (Woodman), 'to constitute and to rule the Isis-Urania Temple No. 3, of the Order of the G.D. in the Outer, and to Initiate and Perfect therein any person Male or Female who has been duly approved of and certified by us. For which purpose this shall be sufficient Warrant.' The original Charter was drawn by Mina Bergson, then a pupil at the Slade School of Fine Art, whose only reward was to become the first initiate of the new temple. She was rapidly followed by some 50 further initiates, the men heavily outweighing the women and drawn largely from masonic circles. A few had come from the ranks of the Theosophical Society which was to prove a fruitful source, especially of women members, once H.P. Blavatsky had been reconciled to the activities of a rival body.

Not all of the early members came from the London area

*The official appointment of Benjamin Cox as 'Hierophant in Weston-super-Mare' (April 1888) and as 'senior of the Three Chiefs' of the Osiris Temple No. 4 (December 1888).*

```
                  ORDER   OF   THE
                       G. D.
                  IN   THE   OUTER.
```

## Osiris Temple, No. 4.

```
    V.H. Frater CRUX-DAT-SALUTEM, 5°—6°, Imperator.
    V.H. Frater EXPECTANS-EXPECTAVI,     Præmonstrator.
    V.H. Frater FIDE,                    Cancellarius.

CARB FRATER _____

        You are requested to be present at a MEETING of
the OSIRIS TEMPLE, to be held at the _____
_____ on _____

the _____ day of _____ 188  .

        The Temple will be Opened at_____

p.m.
                    AGENDA :
The Ceremony of the 0—0 grade at_____ p.m.
    „      „      „    1—10 grade at_____ p.m.
    „      „      „    2—9 grade at_____ p.m.
    „      „      „    3—8 grade at_____ p.m.
    „      „      „    4—6 grade at_____ p.m.
The Festival & Ceremony of the_____Equinox_____ p.m.
              (By Order),
                      FIDE,
                        Cancellarius.

Dated_____ 188  .
```

*Printed summons for meetings of the Osiris Temple.*

and some were eager for temples of their own. Benjamin Cox, the Borough Treasurer of the seaside resort of Weston-super-Mare, had known Westcott in his days as a young pharmacist at Martock in Somerset and had long been associated with him in a number of obscure masonic Rites and Orders. He was initiated into Isis-Urania during March 1888 and soon brought in six of his local masonic colleagues. On 8 October, Westcott issued a decree authorising Cox to set up a temple in his home town; by December a name had been chosen and on the 5th of that month the Chiefs of the Second Order chartered the 'Osiris Temple No. 4 of Somersetshire' with 'Very Honoured Frater Crux Dat Salutem' (Benjamin Cox) as its Hierophant. But for some reason unknown – perhaps by virtue of the lack of bracing air at Weston-super-Mare, or because of lethargy on the part of the Order's

West Country initiates – the Osiris Temple proved to be a frail creation. It never had more than 12 members and within two years was in a state of decline. In 1895 Benjamin Cox died, the Charter was returned to Westcott and the surviving members resumed their mundane lives. The other temple chartered in 1888 was to prove more resilient, and far more troublesome.

Among the members of the S.R.I.A. who joined the Golden Dawn in its early days was T.H. Pattinson (Frater Vota Vita Mea in the Order), a watchmaker of Baildon in Yorkshire and who was not, as A.E. Waite described him, 'one who made spectacles'. Pattinson urged upon Westcott the suitability of Bradford as a home for a temple of the Order. He also cautioned Westcott about accepting candidates too readily and sent him an account of an astral vision in support of his viewpoint. This vision mightily impressed Mathers who transcribed and embellished it and furthered with it his own fantasies about the Secret Chiefs. Pattinson's advice was accepted and on 19 October, 1888, Horus Temple No. 5 was consecrated at Bradford. As with Osiris, its membership was initially all male, the first initiation of a woman not being until some years later. Soror Vi et Fide was also Mrs Pattinson and as she progressed only to the grade of Zelator she may have joined solely out of curiosity. It would be interesting to know what she made of her husband's vision – with or without Mather's embroidery:

> Copy of Communication from the Inner Ring, made to Fra. Vota Vita Mea, given in his letter June 20, 1888 to Fra Sapere Aude:

> The *Crowned One* gave to Fras. V.V.M. and H. [presumably F.D. Harrison] much information concerning the natural creation and the following symbol was the one he adopted to illustrate primary creation or the union of first causes:

> After this Fra. H was conducted by an Eagle-headed messenger into the presence of the Angel R + [Raphael] (whom I, S'Rioghail Mo Dhream, know by the motto L[ux] e T[enebris]) He said:

'I wish to speak to you of the G.D. The prime mover of it must exercise the keenest possible care, and must not accept people into its secrets who are not Occult Students, they all ought to have some occult development which has been the outcome of their own research; otherwise much Evil Magic will be the result. Much good can come out of it if rightly directed, but *one* Evil One can upset the Harmony of the whole, so that its efforts would be neutral for a lengthy period. *The Idea in view* must be not to *establish an Order,* but *to gather together those men who are an Order in themselves.* Understand that the G.D. is *MY Order* and that I am and must be accountable for it. The *last one* initiated [Dr T.W. Coffin, who left the Order within a year having remained in the grade of Neophyte] must be considered and allowed to wait before giving information; 2 or 3 others also are not of much use, and others are likely to drop out. You must take every care not to initiate any who have no occult tendency in a degree developed. Convey my message to those who can carry out my advice.

'You must consider yourselves highly favoured indeed for being allowed to come in contact with the one (the Crowned One) you did tonight.

'Also I would caution and advise you to be *very* careful in the use of Divine Names, and all symbols should (be) correctly traced. I have seen this lady in Switzerland whom you have been trying to release. I confirm the work you have attempted. But you have failed to fully carry out your intention. The failure is due to the want of correctness in carrying out your Ritual. When the Divine Names are used *they are made operative by the Emotion of the Soul;* if uttered by a cold soul-starved man they are of no use. Put your soul-power into them, and let your whole being speak them; then they *do* become operative; and the final issue of this lady in Switzerland is left open at present for your instruction. You have discovered and commanded the assailants, but you have not yet subdued them; although she will be very carefully watched now. You must make your promise of protection a fact, and establish it as a permanent operation. I shall see you again as to this.'

He also said: – 'The G.D. will soon find the prime movers plenty to do; they will have more applicants than they can take; and if not careful will get beyond their control.'

*Provisional By-Laws for Horus Temple. Semper Fidelis was J. Leech Atherton, and the annotations are by Westcott (Sapere Aude).*

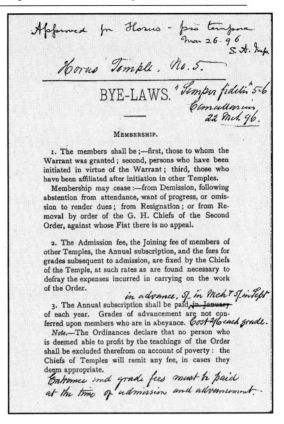

Approved for Horus - pro tempore
Mar 26 · 96
S. A. Imp.

**Horus Temple. No. 5.**

**BYE-LAWS.** Semper fidelis 5·6
Cancellarius
22 Mch 96.

MEMBERSHIP.

1.—The members shall be;—first, those to whom the Warrant was granted; second, persons who have been initiated in virtue of the Warrant; third, those who have been affiliated after initiation in other Temples.

Membership may cease:—from Demission, following abstention from attendance, want of progress, or omission to render dues; from Resignation; or from Removal by order of the G. H. Chiefs of the Second Order, against whose Fiat there is no appeal.

2. The Admission fee, the Joining fee of members of other Temples, the Annual subscription, and the fees for grades subsequent to admission, are fixed by the Chiefs of the Temple, at such rates as are found necessary to defray the expenses incurred in carrying on the work of the Order.

*in advance, £ in Mch & £ in Sept*
3. The Annual subscription shall be paid, ~~in January~~ of each year. Grades of advancement are not conferred upon members who are in abeyance. *Cost 2/6 each grade.*

*Note.*—The Ordinances declare that no person who is deemed able to profit by the teachings of the Order shall be excluded therefrom on account of poverty: the Chiefs of Temples will remit any fee, in cases they deem appropriate.

*Entrance and grade fees must be paid at the time of admission and advancement.*

**He then said to Fra. H., 'You can go'; and the Eagle-headed Messenger conducted him back.**

The Angel was evidently perceptive, for the number of new members did increase precipitately and the two new temples proved to be essential. Whether Westcott approved of adepts other than himself and Mathers receiving messages from the Secret Chiefs is another matter. More immediate disapproval of the Golden Dawn came from another quarter. Many members, including those from masonic circles, were also theosophists and Mme Blavatsky viewed the growth of the new Order with some alarm, believing that it would siphon off those of her own members with a penchant for practical occultism.

To counter any possible threat, she launched, in October 1888, the Esoteric Section of the Theosophical Society, which hinted at the 'acquisition of occult powers and the conquest of

*Private*

> 3/6. Camden Road N.
>
> Nov 2. 92.
>
> Care F vel S,
>
> The 'V. H. Præmonstator of the HORUS Temple G.D. has resigned his office; two of the members have sent in their resignations of membership; and one frater has been suspended.
>
> Under these circumstances, the Chiefs of the Second Order have instructed me to take charge of the Temple until it has once more its Three Chiefs:
>
> Please to attend on Sunday November 13th at Three p.m. when I shall be present, and will explain the decisions which have been arrived at. The Chiefs feel full confidence in the fidelity of the Officers and members of the Temple; and I shall be willing to admit to the Grade of Neophyte, any approved Candidate who may be in attendance.
>
> Yours fraternally
>
> Sapere aude . 5 = 6

*Official letter from Westcott (1892), announcing his taking charge of Horus Temple.*

the secrets of nature' and utilised a 'Probationers Pledge' that emphasized secrecy 'as regards the signs and passwords of the School and all confidential documents'. In this way those seeking glamour could find it within the T.S. She further instructed members of the Esoteric Section not to join any other occult order and to give up their existing memberships. But warfare with the Theosophical Society was avoided through the action of one who was probably the Golden Dawn's most timid member.

Not that he intended to challenge Mme Blavatsky's authority, for the Revd. William Alexander Ayton was far too timorous for so positive an act, but when told that if he wished to remain in the Esoteric Section then he must give up his membership of the Golden Dawn, he 'felt bound to do so at once without hesitation, and write to some of my Yorkshire chelas, who belonged to it and the T.S., to do the same'. They however, were made of sterner stuff and although dismayed by Mme Blavatsky's order,

*Circular letter to members
of the Horus Temple
(1900). The malaise in the
Order was clearly not
confined to Isis-Urania.*

**HORUS TEMPLE No. 5.**

*October 6th, 1900.*

CARE FRATER,

At the last regular meeting of this Temple it was resolved to take a room, in Bradford, to be used as a head centre for the development of such occult projects as would be of interest to the general body of members, but more especially for the promotion of advanced study.

Although the vote for this purpose was unanimous, and £10 14s. was voluntarily subscribed towards £12, which was asked for, yet, the undercurrent of the meeting was *not* in accordance with that *harmonious* and confident zeal which has been so characteristic of the " Horus " brotherhood in the past, and which has, undoubtedly, been the basis of its progress.

Under these conditions the undersigned do not feel confident in recommending the adoption of this resolution, at present, but think it advisable to leave it over for further consideration at our next regular meeting, if found desirable.

We shall be glad to have your opinion on this matter.

Yours fraternally,

T. H. PATTINSON, *Imperator.*
B. E. J. EDWARDS, *Præmonstrator.*
J. K. GARDNER, *Sub-Præmonstrator.*
J. L. ATHERTON, *Cancellarius.*

BEECH GROVE,
BINGLEY.

promptly marched off as a deputation to remonstrate with her so that 'H.P.B. [Madame Blavatsky] then began to see she had made a mistake and she wrote to me for advice, which I gave, and the consequence was, she withdrew this ukase as regards the Rosicrucian Society'. Nor was this all, for 'Dr Wynn Westcott, the head of this Rosicrucian Society, joined the Esoteric Section of the T.S. and with him some 20 others, and about 14 from Yorkshire. All is well that ends well!' So Ayton reported to his friend F.L. Gardner, but an end to the Order's troubles it most certainly was not.

While Westcott was certainly pleased with the new harmony between the Golden Dawn and the Theosophical Society, not all the Horus members were as concerned as Ayton's 'Yorkshire Chelas'. By 1892 there was a decided split in the Temple's ranks, with theosophists on one hand and Rosicrucians on the other. In a vain attempt to pour oil on troubled waters, Westcott sent Annie Horniman (Soror Fortiter et Recte) to the September equinox meeting of Horus to appeal to the better nature of the squabbling members and also, if necessary, to admonish them. Her subsequent report to Westcott singled out two of the theosophical faction for censure. One of them, Oliver Firth, whom Col. Olcott, the co-founder of the Theosophical Society, described as 'that joyous-hearted, keen-brained friend', had all the qualities that Westcott preferred not to see among the adepts. He was insubordinate: 'When requested by the Hierophant to act as auditor he refused rudely and disrespectfully and sitting down suddenly he exclaimed "I shan't", and showed an independence of mind'. He referred to astrology as, 'mere divination' and he showed 'a rebellious wish to pick and choose his subjects of study'. Frater Firth objected to wearing 'the sash of his grade in the Temple because of its similarity to Free Masonry'. Worst of all he was guilty of 'Speaking disrespectfully of our Ceremonies'. A newly inducted frater referred to 'the want of reverence on the part of some of the spectators at his Initiation' (at the Equinox Ceremony) and 'said how it lost in solemnity'. Frater Firth, 'instead of expressing penitence gloried in doing as he felt inclined in the Temple and said he would laugh there if he chose, even if turned out for so doing'. 'Such a speech', thought Miss Horniman, 'is bad enough in itself, but being made before Neophytes and other low grade Fratres and Sorores is destructive to their discipline.'

Nor was Firth alone in his 'deeply rooted insubordination'. F.D. Harrison, one of Horus Temple's first members, had also misbehaved. He 'sat in a lower place than his 3 = 8 grade allows and was a source of or a party to an unquietness during the 0 = 0 Ceremony'. Not content with this he 'referred in a most disrespectful way to both communications read that day in open Temple', adding that the expulsion of Miss O'Connell (Soror Ciall Agus Niart, who had fallen out with Mina Mathers) was 'a mere squabble between two women' and compounding his sins by speaking 'as if the Ceremonies were only foolish mummeries

*Official notice (1894) from Mathers announcing the suspension of Theresa O'Connell. Four years later she gave Westcott a detailed statement about the foundation of the Golden Dawn in which she denied Mathers' authority.*

### G. D.
#### Private and Confidential.

The G.H. Chiefs of the Second Order having in the exercise of the discretion vested in them by the Laws of the Order, suspended from membership, Miss Theresa O'Connell, who is known by the motto of Giall agus neart, earnestly desire to call your attention to the terms of your pledge of fidelity, by which you are bound to treat her as a entire outsider; and that you are therefore prohibited from disclosing to her either the dates or place of meeting, the business transacted, or the names of candidates or of members present or absent, as well as from placing in her hands, or showing to her any ritual, lecture, or manuscript relating to the Order, or its knowledge, and that if you disclose to her, (or to any other person who is not in possession of the Pass Word) any of these points, you will be liable to the penalties provided for breach of the conditions of your membership. This prohibition remains in force as to C.A.N., until you receive notice in Writing of her re-instatement.

### Signed, DEO DUCE COMITE FERRO, 7-4,
Chief of the College of the Adepti in Anglia.

The following persons have resigned their membership, and so will not be any longer in possession of the Pass Word, nor in communion with the Order.

Oliver Firth, Florence Firth, Alfred Monck, Emily K. Bates, W. M. Farquhar, Jessie L Horne, Francis D. Harrison, John Midgeley, Selim Mosaili, Mahomet Eusouf.

NON OMNIS MORIAR, 7-4, Registrar.

in his eyes'. This was somewhat hypocritical for a man who would go on to become Grand Secretary of Annie Besant's 'Universal Co-Masonry', perhaps with a wish to recapture the splendid ceremonies that he missed when he and Oliver Firth were both expelled from the Golden Dawn soon after Miss Horniman had submitted her report.

Two months after this visit, Westcott himself went to Bradford and delivered a long, stirring address to the members of Horus, to be followed in March 1893 by Mathers – who threatened the Temple with suspension if members did not stop relaying accounts of their doings to the impenitent Oliver Firth. He urged them not to see the Golden Dawn and Theosophical

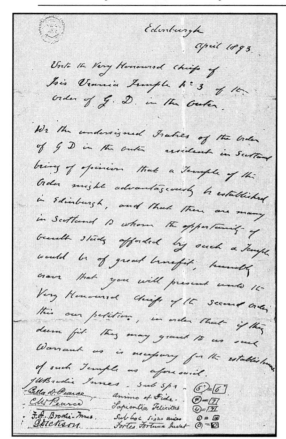

*The application for a warrant for the Amen-Ra Temple at Edinburgh (1893).*

Society as being in opposition and then 'dwelt at some length on the solemnity to be observed in the Ceremonies', and reminded them of 'the humility and self-denial necessary in every true Occultist'.

It would have been well if Mathers had himself taken this reminder to heart, for it was to be his own inflated ego that would eventually bring down not just one temple but the whole Order. And the Order was growing. Not only were new temples springing up – Amen-Ra at Edinburgh in 1893; and Ahathoor at Paris early in 1894 – but by 1892 a new dimension had been added with the creation of rituals for the inner, Rosicrucian Order: the *Rosae Rubeae at Aureae Crucis*. The adept grades had existed in theory from the beginning, but they were conferred without the benefit of ceremony until December 1891,

*Notice concerning subscriptions, with a caution as to entry into Mark Masons' Hall in London (c. 1893).*

## NOTICE.

The Annual Subscription of 10/- becomes due at the Vernal Equinox. This can either be paid personally by Members on the 21st inst., or be remitted to the present Cancellarius of the I.V. Temple,

V. H. Fra. Levavi Oculos,

5=6,

to whom all communications should be addressed in the following way:—

" P. W. BULLOCK,

22, Upper George Street,

Bryanston Square, W."

N.B. — Please note that you must not enter Mark Masons' Hall by the front door, but go under archway and down passage, entering by a door on the right.

when Annie Horniman attained the grade of Adeptus Minor, even though 'the roof was not on the vault and the paint on the crook and scourge was wet' as she told A.E. Waite some 20 years later. To remain true to the myth of Christian Rosencreutz, the vault, which was a central feature of the Rosicrucian tradition, was essential, but the ceremonies were new and original, brought into the World of Action through the genius of Mathers.

Most members of the Golden Dawn were unconcerned with the Inner or Second Order, being quite content to work their way up through the rituals of the Outer Order and to absorb just as much of theoretical occultism as would keep them safely sure of their superiority over their fellow men. Those who wanted more than this were of a different breed. By the end of 1896 the Golden Dawn had some 300 members, of whom less than one-third progressed to the Inner Order, while even fewer played an active role within it. But those few (never more than 60) formed a potentially disruptive core: enthusiastic but of independent mind, they were not inclined to accept unquestioned the dictates of an increasingly autocratic and eccentric Chief. Mathers may have been the creator of the Inner Order, but its adepts were not his creatures; nor were they mere occultists, for, unlike the Outer Order, the R.R. at A.C. was wholly magical, and those who attained it were magicians.

Initially, all went well in the Second Order. Members' progress was governed by the official manuscript rituals and instructions provided by Westcott and Mathers, and by the less formal 'Flying Rolls' – the more speculative papers in which other adepts also had a hand. Most of the Order activities were carried out at the vault in Thavies Inn, Holborn (later at Clipstone Street), and recorded in the Order Diary, together with much trivial information on the day-to-day management of the vault. For four years the members busied themselves with rituals, examinations, and their highly original approach to spiritual development. But happy harmony was not to prevail.

In addition to being an occultist, Mina Mathers was also an art student of great promise. In 1892 Annie Horniman, who had been Mina's closest friend when she was Miss Bergson, and who recognised her talent, offered to give her money in order to study in Paris. The offer was taken up and Mina departed for France in May – but accompanied by her husband who also expected to be funded, which was far from Miss Horniman's original intention. She had been giving money to the Mathers while they were still in England and over a period of five years Annie Horniman doled out more than £1,300 only to see it used more to further Mathers' occult fantasies than to assist his wife's career as an artist. At first he had been appreciative of the money and showed his gratitude by inviting Annie to consecrate the new Ahathoor Temple, but as demands upon her purse increased a mutual irritation developed. She was unhappy with what she saw as 'impure and mischievous' sexual doctrines on the part of another Order member – Dr E.W. Berridge – and complained loudly about them within the Order. Annie Horniman formed the mistaken impression that Mathers tacitly supported Berridge's ideas even though on one occasion Berridge's behaviour so annoyed him that Mathers temporarily suspended him from membership. Mathers' reaction was one of impatience. In January 1896 he wrote reproving her for her presumption in assuming that her opinions were necessarily those of others; reminding her that within the Order she was Soror Fortiter et Recte and not Miss Horniman, Mathers asked her,

> whenever matters of *sex* arise in the Order, and you are asked for instruction thereon; to refer them to G.H. Frater N.O.M. [Dr Westcott] and not judge them yourself, until you can do so *apart* from your outer personality.

Annie reassured him that she was not impugning his honour, to which he replied with his usual want of tact, telling her cheerfully that he and Mina had assumed 'that you were temporarily (and unintentionally no doubt) giving way to an unbalanced condition of mind which would be likely to ultimate in a condition favourable to the condition of a mania. [In which case] the only honourable action evident to be taken, was to check your state of mind, and that sharply, promptly and at whatever cost.'

Annie managed somehow to swallow what Mathers wrote, but not his growing Celtic-fringe political obsessions, which were being paid for with her money. As she wrote to William Peck, a prominent member of Amen-Ra,

> The feeling that my honour as an upright person was being injured by supporting a political movement of which I did not approve, grew too strong to be borne.

She then told the Mathers that no more money would be forthcoming, to which Mathers responded by laying unjust charges against her. In September 1896 she resigned from her post of Sub-Praemonstrator (Instructor) of Isis-Urania.

Mathers' next move was to issue a long, rambling and

bizarre 'Manifesto' in which he demanded that all Theorici Adepti Minores (those adepts who had passed the series of pre-scribed examinations) submit themselves utterly to his will in respect of all Order affairs, justifying his demand by claiming that he was the one great adept chosen to work under the Secret Chiefs and to transmit their commands: 'I cannot con-ceive a much less advanced Initiate being able to support such a strain even for five minutes, without Death ensuing.' But of these Secret Chiefs he could tell the adepts nothing:

> I do not even know their earthly names.
>
> I know them only by certain secret mottoes.
>
> I have *but very rarely* seen them in the physical body; and on such rare occasions *the rendezvous was made astrally by them* at the time and place which had been astrally appointed beforehand.
>
> For my part I believe them to be human and living upon this earth; but possessing terrible superhuman powers.

For most of the adepti this explanation was sufficient and Mathers received their 'thorough and complete submission', but not from Annie Horniman. Unwilling to accept either his absolute authority or the continual drain on her purse, she offered a partial acceptance of his demands but refused to make further handouts. The enraged Mathers immediately expelled her from the Order – only to find that 30 members had prompt-ly signed a petition for her reinstatement; however, the petition was not, in the end, sent to him and Annie remained in exile. The time for Mathers' will to be thwarted had not yet arrived.

Further problems soon arose. In February 1897, Westcott, who had for some years been content to act as Registrar for the Order, was appointed Vice-Imperator of Isis-Urania. But he was not destined to remain in this exalted office for long. Within six weeks he had resigned from all offices in the Golden Dawn, because, as he told his friend and ally F.L. Gardner:

> It had somehow become known to the State officers that I was a prominent official of a society in which I had been foolishly posturing

## ORDER OF THE G∴D∴ IN THE OUTER.
### ISIS-URANIA TEMPLE, NO: 3.

*All changes of address should be sent to the following Officials:* —

**MRS. PERCY WILLIAM BULLOCK,**
*69 Thornton Avenue, Bedford Park, London; W∴*
Who calls the Meetings; and collects the Fees.

**MARCUS WORSLEY BLACKDEN, ESQ:**
*7 Grove Street, North, Norwich:*
Who circulates Rituals and Knowledge-Lectures.

**HERBERT CROSSLEY MORRIS ESQ:**
*361 Brixton Rd., S:W:*
who conducts Exams. from $0^0=0^0$ to $4^0=7^0$.

**MRS. JOHN RAND,**
*Elmfield, Esher, Surrey:*
who conducts Exams. from $4^0=7^0$ to $5^0=6^0$.

The Entrance Fee is £ 2 » 2 » 0 .
The Annual Subscription is £ 1 •
N.B. As regards those in poor or reduced circumstances — half
fees are accepted, or even all money payments remitted.

$\mathcal{V}$ ∴ $\mathcal{H}$ ∴ $\mathcal{F}$ ∴ " *ANIMA PURA SIT* " has left England.

*Official Notice for members of Isis-Urania in 1898*

as one possessed of magical powers – and that if this became more public it would not do for a Coroner of the Crown to be made shame of in such a mad way.

Or, as Aleister Crowley more picturesquely put it, the authorities 'intimated to Dr Westcott that he was paid to sit on corpses, not to raise them; and that he must choose between his Coronership and his Adeptship'. Westcott thought that someone was talking, although he had no idea 'who it is that persecutes me'. Three years later he was to find out.

A chastened Westcott did not result in the smooth running of the Order. The members of Horus resented 'dogmatic control' from London and in 1898 they asked Mathers to take charge of their Second Order workings. As T.H. Pattinson informed Gardner, who seems to have been both universal busybody and universal confidante, 'You have no need to fear Mathers getting the top end of the Horus Temple chaps'. Worse disagreements arose in Amen-Ra at Edinburgh, where a few members supported Mathers while the majority fell into two opposing camps (under Peck and J.W. Brodie-Innes respectively) who both rejected Mathers while cordially detesting each other. In Isis-Urania serious trouble had begun to brew, although it was not yet realised what was afoot, on 18 November, 1898, when Aleister Crowley was initiated into the Golden Dawn. Frater Perdurabo, as he was known in the Order, soon advanced through the grades of the Outer Order, becoming a 4 = 7 Philosophus in the following May; but he was refused admittance to the Second Order because the more perceptive adepti had recognised his failings – both magical and sexual – and realised what trouble would follow in his wake. Mathers had no such compunction and was, in any case, an outstandingly poor judge of character. He admitted Crowley to the R.R. at A.C. in Paris on 16 January, 1900. If nothing else, it gave him an ally for the battles ahead.

By this time dissension in Isis-Urania had grown to such a pitch that some members wished to close it down. It was evidently in connection with this dispute that Florence Farr wrote to Mathers. His reply was not what she had expected:

N.B. – Read this letter carefully before showing any part of it to anyone!

16 February 1900

C. et V.H. Soror S.S.D.D. Sapientia Sapienti Dono Data

My time is just now so enormously occupied with the arrangements for the Buildings and Decorations of the Egyptian Temple of Isis in Paris, as well as other matters, that I *must* write as briefly as possible.

(a) I have never wished to interfere in your private affairs, but if you choose to bring mine into a discussion in a Second Order meeting, the matter concerns me as well as yourself.

(b) As you did not date your letter to me, and as I received it on the 13th January, 1900, it was difficult for me to conceive that it had been written *after* instead of before the meeting on the 12th. I possess a copy of the minutes of that meeting.

(c) *I refuse definitely* to close Isis-Urania Temple, and am prepared to receive the resignations from their offices of those chiefs who no longer wish to serve as such. I can understand in your case, that in addition to your somewhat heavy work in the Second Order, holding office in Isis has been an additional load.

(d) Now, with regard to the Second Order, it would be with the *very greatest regret* both from my personal regard for you, as well as from the occult standpoint that I should receive your Resignation as my Representative in the Second Order in London; but I cannot let you form a combination to make a schism therein with the idea of working secretly or avowedly under 'Sapere Aude' [Westcott] under the mistaken impression that he received an Epitome of Second Order work from G.H. Soror 'Sapiens Dominabitur Astris'. For this forces me to tell you plainly (and understand me well, I can prove to the hilt every word which I here say and more, and were I confronted with S.A., I should say the same), though for the sake of the Order, and for the circumstance that it would mean so deadly a blow to S.A.'s reputation, I entrust you to keep this secret from the *Order*, for the present at least, though you are at perfect liberty to show *him* this if you think fit, *after mature consideration.*

(e) He has NEVER been *at any time* either in personal, or in written communication with the Secret Chiefs of the Order, he having *either himself forged or procured to be forged* the professed correspondence between him and them, and my tongue having been tied all these years by a previous Oath of Secrecy to him, demanded by him, from me, before showing me what he had either done or caused to be done or both. – You must comprehend from what little I say here, the *extreme gravity* of such a matter, and again I ask you, both for his sake and that of the Order, not to force me to go farther into the subject.

I again reiterate that *every atom* of the knowledge of the Order has come *through me alone* from 0–0 to 5–6 inclusive, and that it is I alone who have been and am in communication with the Secret Chiefs of the Order.

51

I may further remark that 'Sapiens Dominabitur Astris' is now in Paris and aiding me with the Isis movement.

Lastly, I again ask you to consider well this letter, and not to put me in such a position that I shall be compelled to act publicly.

Yours in fraternity and sincerity,

Deo Duce Comite Ferro

7 = 4

Chief of the Second Order

The 'Sapiens Dominabitur Astris' then aiding Mathers was, of course, not the mythical Anna Sprengel but the rascally Madame Horos; something quite unknown to the adepts of Isis-Urania. To them the letter was a bombshell.

If Mathers' allegations were true then the whole Order was a sham based on forgery and deceit, and publication of his claims would lead to the Order's collapse. It was thus essential for the London adepts both to discover the truth of the matter and to keep it from the membership at large. The few Second Order members whom Florence Farr did tell formed an investigating committee, but there was little that they could do since Mathers refused to enlarge on his accusations, and Westcott proved evasive.

Westcott could have defended himself more strongly – he had a series of affidavits concerning his apparent receipt of the Anna Sprengel letters and his primacy in the Order – but he chose not to do so. He merely told W.B. Yeats, who had been deputised to approach him, that 'Speaking *legally*, I find I cannot prove the details of the origin of the knowledge and history of the G.D., so I should not be just or wise to bias your opinion of them'. Westcott's own notes of their meeting indicate that he relied on legal advice:

March 20, 1900

W.B. Yeats called and said that the Isis Temple GD was in a very disturbed state and a committee had been appointed and was considering whether to secede from Mr Mathers or to throw him off. W. said he had retired years ago from the

Order, promising M. a free hand and that W. could not
interfere with him, & now just because M. did mad things –
W. could not cut in again. M. cannot prove his charges, but
on the other hand W. cannot prove the truth of the history –
& his lawyer considers W. should abstain from any statement
until compelled to enter into controversy – W. therefore
declined to make any statement as to M.'s new attitude
because if he denied it that would involve his calling M. a liar
on the other hand – if he confessed to M.'s new tale that
would be to say Dr Woodman was a liar and Mrs Woodman
would have a grievance – Yeats said he represented the
Committee but declined to give their names – W. said he
could not interfere and must allow, if necessary, opinion to
go against him – because his witnesses being dead he could
not disprove anything.

Yeats' record of this meeting was more telling:

> SA remembers what he himself said fairly though not
> completely; but less correctly what I said. I went to ask him
> to tell what he knew about the origin of the documents
> D.D.C.F. declared to be forged. I made it plain to him that
> D.D.C.F. would have to substantiate his charges or withdraw
> them, or clear out. When I found that S.A was afraid to meet
> the charges in any way I said – here I remember my exact
> words 'your silence will have a very bad effect on the
> committee'. But has he heard I said the tales of D.D.C.F.
> being 'erratic'? He said 'you have a mad man for chief what
> more can you expect' D.E.D.I .[Demon est Deus Inversus:
> Yeats' motto in the Order] June 6 1900.

Mathers, on his part, was in a fury over the investigation
and peremptorily, if impotently, forbade its continuation, adding
in his letter to Percy Bullock this amazing comment:

> Some of you have been pleased to remark that I have condoned a
> felony. I would sooner condone any number of offences against
> the Law of Man, than I would fail in the first duty of an Occultist,
> which is Fraternity and Fidelity, and it is the want of these in the
> English Order which has been the root of all mischief.

Document XI (d)

15, RANDOLPH ROAD,
MAIDA VALE, W.,
*Monday, April 23rd.*

The Envoy of G. H. Frater Deo Duce Comite
Ferro, 7° - 4° Chief of the S.O., unto all
members of the London Branch of the S.O.

GREETING.

It is first fitting that I express my sincere regret that
members of the S. O. should have been put to unnecessary
trouble.

In defiance of a promise given by Mrs. Emery, Miss
Cracknell, and Mr. Hunter, to V.H. Soror Fidelis and V.H.
Frater Pedurabo, the rooms were forced open and various
property of mine detained, while the projected interviews
were made impossible.

The Courts of Law will shortly decide further concerning this action.

It should be mentioned that the story of the masked
man is altogether untrue.

I hereby suspend V.H. Sorores S.S.D.D., and Tempus
Omnia Revelat, and V.H. Fratres Hora et Semper, Levavi
Oculos, and Demon est Deus Inversus, from both orders.

I must now request that an appointment be made
with me by each individual member of the S.O., and at the
above address.

Letters may be addressed to Miss Elaine Simpson.

Failing this, or a serious and reasonable excuse, suspension from both orders will operate automatically at
noon on ~~Saturday.~~ *14 so day*

My authority for this action will be shown to each
member on arriving at the interview.

Witness my Seal.

28²

*Aleister Crowley's printed circular demanding the attendance of Second Order members at Blythe Road during the Rebellion of 1900. None of the members responded to the summons.*

He followed this up with an attempt to seize the Second Order vault, at 36 Blythe Road, Hammersmith, and the properties of the Order, and an even more futile attempt to obtain the absolute submission of the members. His chosen emissary for this foray was Aleister Crowley, who arrived in London on 14 April to carry out Mathers' impossible orders. The farcical events that followed have been so often recounted and so often exaggerated, that they are best presented in the sparse but accurate form of the Second Order's Statement of Recent Events:

> On April 17th, Aleister Crowley, *alias* Count Vladimir Svareff, *alias* Aleister MacGregor, otherwise known as Perdurabo, a member of the 4–7 Grade of the Isis-Urania Temple in company with Soror Donorum Dei Dispensatio Fidelis, 5–6, forced the door of the Headquarters of the Second Order,

changed the locks, and endeavoured to prevent other members entering.

D.D.D.F. then summoned the Members of the 5–6 Grade to personal and separate interviews, showing a statement by D.D.C.F. concerning the appointment by him of an 'Envoy' whose identity was concealed, but who ultimately was proved to be the said Perdurabo; every effort being made to cause the Second Order to believe that the Envoy was some unknown person.

In spite of the reasons given for this concealment by D.D.C.F., it is evident that the true reason was, that Perdurabo has never been legally advanced to the Portal nor admitted to the 5–6 Grade, and D.D.C.F. well knew he was a person undeserving of confidence.

On the day appointed for these interviews, the said Perdurabo arrived at the Second Order rooms. He was dressed in Highland dress, a black mask over his face, a plaid thrown over his head and shoulders, an enormous gold or gilt cross on his breast, and a dagger at his side. All this melodramatic nonsense was of course designed in the hope that it would cause members to sign a pledge of allegiance to D.D.C.F. He was, however, stopped by the landlord, and compelled to leave by the Fratres H.E.S. [Hora et Semper: E.A. Hunter] and D.E.D.I. assisted by a policeman.

Thus rebuffed, Crowley attempted to obtain the Order properties by legal action but soon withdrew from this compounding of his folly, and the Second Order in London threw off the yoke of the paranoid Mathers and his equally odd companions. To the other members they pointed out that:

From these various circumstances it will be seen that D.D.C.F. as Chief of the Order, has placed himself in an untenable position. If his accusation of forgery be true, he has knowingly, and on his own showing for many years made use of that forgery as the warrant for his authority as Chief; if his statement be false, he has been guilty of a slander on one to whom he was bound by the most solemn pledges of fraternity and fidelity, both as a member of this Order and as a Freemason.

In either case, the conduct has been such as absolutely to destroy the confidence of the Second Order in London.

Therefore the Second Order in London (between 50 and 60 members) is, with the exception of five members, unanimously resolved that it will no longer acknowledge D.D.C.F. as Chief of the Order, and that its connection with him is absolutely severed.

The original draft of the Statement was more blunt: 'The members after waiting until the 21st of April, resolved to take the matter into their own hands. The result is that a Revolution has taken place.' With Mathers thus deposed, a single Chief would no longer rule them all; the old system of three Chiefs was revived, supported by a Council of ten. All very correct, no doubt, in terms of kabbalistic symbolism, but possessed of little power. Mathers may well have been quite mad, but he was undoubtedly a magical genius, and without him no magical light shone within the Order. From the day of his expulsion the old Golden Dawn was dead.

# CHAPTER THREE

# The Magical Pilgrim's Progress

'Child of Earth, unpurified and unconsecrated, thou canst not enter the path of the West.'

So the Kerux (or Herald) halted the Neophyte after the Temple had been solemnly opened, the candidate introduced and his Obligation – worded exactly as revealed at the Horos trial – repeated. The ceremony continued in this manner:

Stolistes: (Signing a cross on Candidate's forehead) Child of Earth, I purify thee with water.

Dadouchos: (Censing Candidate) Child of Earth, I consecrate thee with fire.

Hegemon: Child of Earth, twice consecrated, thou mayest approach the gate of the West. (They move to the West, facing Throne and halt. Hiereus rises takes banner in left hand, menaces Candidate with sword and says as the Hegemon slips up the Candidate's hoodwink.)

Hiereus: 'Thou canst not pass me by' saith the Guardian of the West unless thou canst tell my name.'

Heg.: Darkness is thy name, the Great One of the Paths of the Shades.

Hiereus: (Slowly sinking point of sword.) Child of Earth, fear is failure. Therefore be without fear, for in the heart of the coward virtue abideth not. Thou hast known me, so pass thou on. (Hoodwink slipped down again, they move to the North and halt.)

| | |
|---|---|
| Kerux: | Child of Earth, unpurified and unconsecrated, thou canst not enter the Path of the East. |
| Stol.: | (Signing a Cross on the Candidate's forehead) Child of Earth, I purify thee with water. |
| Dad.: | (Censing the Candidate) Child of Earth, I consecrate thee with fire. |
| Heg.: | Child of Earth, thrice consecrated, thou mayest approach the gate of the East. (They move to the East facing Throne and halt. Hierophant rises, takes Banner in left hand and raises Sceptre as if to strike. Hegemon slips up Candidate's hoodwink.) |
| Hiero.: | 'Thou canst not pass me by' saith the Guardian of the East, 'unless thou canst tell me my name.' |
| Heg.: | Light dawning in darkness is thy name, the light of a golden day. |
| Hiero.: | (Slowly lowering Sceptre) Child of Earth, remember that unbalanced force is evil, unbalanced mercy is but weakness, unbalanced severity is but oppression. Thou hast known me, so pass thou on unto the Cubical Altar of the Universe. (Hoodwink slipped down and Candidate taken to West of Altar. Hierophant leaves Throne and stands between the pillars, facing Candidate with Sceptre in right hand and Banner in left. Hegemon on Candidate's right. Kerux behind Candidate, Stolistes and Dadouchos right and left of Kerux. All rise.) Let the Candidate kneel while I invoke the Lord of the Universe (Candidate kneels). Lord of the Universe the Vast and the Mighty One, Ruler of Light and Darkness, we adore thee and we invoke thee. Look with favour upon this Neophyte, who now kneeleth before Thee and grant Thine aid unto the higher aspirations of his soul, so that he may prove a true and faithful Frater among us unto the Glory of Thy Ineffable Name. Amen. Let the Candidate rise. Child of Earth, long has thou dwelt in darkness. Quit the |

*May, 1900.*

## R. R. A. C. IN LONDON.

### SECOND ORDER BYE-LAWS.

#### MEMBERSHIP.

1. The members shall be those Adepti whose names are now upon the roll, and those Lords and Ladies of the Portal or Adepti of other Temples who shall be added by the permission of the Executive Council.

2. Candidates for the Outer must be introduced by a Philosophus, or a Lord or Lady of the Portal, but preferably by an Adept, who will state his conviction as to the suitability of the person.
The candidate will be interviewed by a Frater and a Soror separately. Another Frater and Soror shall then make separate clairvoyant investigations. These five reports shall be laid before the Executive Council for their final decision.

3. The Executive Council consists of:—the Moderator, the Scribe, and the Warden ; the seven Adepti

2

Litterati ; and the Three Chiefs of I. U. T. and the Hierophant, Hiereus, and Hegemon of I. U. T. These officers shall be first nominated by the 12 most advanced members of the second Order, then chosen by the Adepti at an annual election.

4. The annual subscription to the Second Order is 10s. 6d., in addition, voluntary donations are accepted from members.
It must be clearly stated at the time of presentation whether gifts of books, furniture, &c., are to be the permanent property of the Order, or merely temporary loans.
Members requiring the return of their loans must formally make request to the Moderator.
The property of the Second Order is vested in two members appointed by the Executive.
The accounts shall be audited annually by two Adepti appointed by the College of Adepts.

5. Resignations are accepted by the Executive. Expulsions can only take place at an Assembly of the College of Adepts by a three-fourths majority, notice having been sent seven days before the meeting to every member.

6. Each Chief of I. U. T. shall have two Subordinates ; who shall be responsible to him for the performance of their duties, with the right of appeal to

*The Bye-Laws of the R.R. et A.C. as revised in 1900.*

3

the Executive Council. One Chief or Sub-Chief must be present to legalise an Outer Order meeting. It is the duty of the Cancellarius to ensure the presence of at least one Chief or Sub-Chief.

7. If ten members wish to hold a special meeting, on receiving their signed petition stating the purpose, the Executive Council shall instruct the Scribe to summon the meeting at a convenient date.

8. All Order intimations must be sent to each member in a separate envelope.
Verbal notices are sufficient when given formally.

9. All Rituals, Lectures, Knowledge Lectures, Side Lectures, Extra Lectures, Ordinances, Bye-Laws and communications from the Cancellarius and other members, must be kept together and preserved in a box, case, or cover, duly labelled and protected from the view and investigation of all outsiders. The label must specifically state that the contents are not personal, and that they are to be sent in case of illness or decease to a certain person, at a certain place ; this nominee should preferably be the Cancellarius.
Each member of the Order undertakes to return to the Cancellarius, *on demand*, all Rituals, Lectures and other MSS. relating to the Order, in case either of his suspension, demission, resignation or expulsion from membership.

4

10. The meeting of R. R. A. C. in London for the election of the Executive Council shall take place not later than the Vernal Equinox of each year.
Financial report to be made on the same occasion.

night and seek the day. (Hoodwink removed and all clap hands. Hierophant, Hiereus, Hegemon join points of Sceptres and Sword above Candidate's head and say together)

| Hierophant | } | Frater . . . we receive thee into this the |
| Hiereus | | Order of the Golden Dawn. |
| Hegemon | | |

In this manner the Neophyte was initiated into the Hermetic Order of the Golden Dawn – utterly bewildered if he or she had come from the ranks of the Theosophical Society, but with a distinct sense of *déjà vu*, as regards the procedures if not the wording of the ceremony, if he was already a Freemason. And just what did he see when the blindfold was removed?

Around the initiate were the ordinary members of the Order in black tunics and black sashes, lettered according to their grades. Before him, in the east, was the double cube of the altar, covered in black and surmounted by a white triangle and the 'Red Cross of Tiphereth', while ranged in their proper places were the officers. Overseeing the temple, but taking no part in the ceremony of initiation, were the three Chiefs of the Order, one of whom must always be present – 'The Imperator to Command, the Praemonstrator to Instruct, the Cancellarius to Record' – all in their robes and regalia. The ceremony itself was the concern of the officers of the temple: the Hierophant, the 'Master of the Hall', set in the east facing the candidate, and resplendent in scarlet mantle and crowned sceptre of red and gold, and bearing the Banner of the East. Below him, seated opposite in the west, was the Hiereus, an 'image of darkness' clothed in 'the black robe of darkness, bearing a white cross upon his left breast'; his lamen (or badge of office) in red and green around his neck, the 'sword of strength and severity' in his hand and the Banner of the West at his side. The third of the principal officers, the Hegemon, whose duty was to lead the neophyte through his reception, was stationed between the two pillars that stood to the east of the cubical altar. He wore a white robe with a red cross on the left breast and bore a red and gold mitre-headed sceptre.

The remaining officers were more prosaic, none having exotic robes but each having a badge of office. First to be

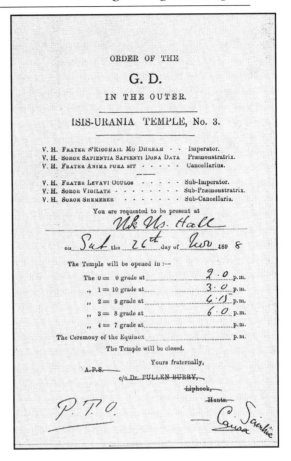

*Each temple issued summonses to members to attend regular meetings. This is a form of summons used by the Isis-Urania Temple – on this occasion for the initiation of Aleister Crowley.*

ORDER OF THE

# G. D.

### IN THE OUTER.

### ISIS-URANIA TEMPLE, No. 3.

V. H. FRATER S'RIOGHAIL MO DHREAM · · · Imperator.
V. H. SOROR SAPIENTIA SAPIENTI DONA DATA  Præmonstratrix.
V. H. FRATER ANIMA PURA SIT · · · · · Cancellarius.

V. H. FRATER LEVAVI OCULOS · · · · · Sub-Imperator.
V. H. SOROR VIGILATE · · · · · · · · Sub-Præmonstratrix.
V. H. SOROR SHEMEBER · · · · · · · · Sub-Cancellaria.

You are requested to be present at

*Mk Ms. Hall*

on *Sat* the *26th* day of *Nov* 189 *8*

The Temple will be opened in :—

The 0 = 0 grade at .................... *9 . 0* p.m.
,, 1 = 10 grade at .................... *3 . 0* p.m.
,, 2 = 9 grade at .................... *4 . 15* p.m.
,, 3 = 8 grade at .................... *6 . 0* p.m.
,, 4 = 7 grade at .................... p.m.

The Ceremony of the Equinox .................... p.m.

The Temple will be closed.

Yours fraternally,

A.P.S.
c/o Dr. PULLEN-BURRY,
Liphook,
Hants.

*P. T. O.*

encountered was the Sentinel, who prepared the candidate for his initiation in an ante-room outside the temple, as would the Tyler of a masonic lodge, on whose office that of the Sentinel was modelled. The candidate would then be brought into the temple by the Hegemon, having been announced by the Kerux, and passed before the Stolistes – 'an image of cold and moisture' – who purified the temple, the members and the candidate with water, and the Dadouchos – who represented 'heat and dryness' and who purified with fire, by way of nothing more alarming than incense.

And the temple itself was carefully laid out. Less complex than the arrangement for the higher grades, that of the Neophyte Grade was yet striking to the initiate: the three Chiefs

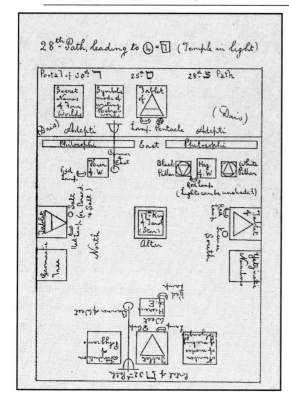

*Temple arranged for 4 = 7 Grade of Philosophus. For each grade of the Outer Order the temple was arranged in a different manner. Printed diagrams were supplied to ensure that everything and everyone were in their proper positions.*

and the Hierophant on their dais, the robed and bedecked officers, the curious pillars and the strange altar. All were designed to represent stages on the kabbalistic Tree of Life. Some of this symbolism was explained to the Neophyte as he went through the remaining part of the ceremony that followed his reception, and he was taught the step, grip, sign and word of the grade, but much of the symbolic interpretation was reserved for special instruction in the Second Order.

The other four grades of the Outer Order – those of 1 = 10 Zelator; 2 = 9 Theoricus; 3 = 8 Practicus; and 4 = 7 Philosophus – were increasingly complex in their workings, involving a symbolic ascent of the Paths on the Tree of Life and an understanding of the appropriate Tarot cards. Each of these grades was also related to one of the four traditional elements (Earth, Air, Water and Fire respectively) with appropriate symbolism utilised in the ceremonies. And there was more. For each grade from Neophyte to Philosophus there was an associated 'Knowledge Lecture' which taught theoretical occultism to the aspirant. The lecture for the Neophyte Grade was extremely basic (not that succeeding lectures were especially advanced) and to the more informed initiate they proved an embarrassment. In his *Confessions,* Aleister Crowley recorded his reaction to them:

> I had been most solemnly sworn to inviolable secrecy. The slightest breach of my oath meant that I should incur 'a deadly and hostile current of will, set in motion by the Greatly Honoured Chiefs of the Second Order, by the which I should fall slain or paralysed, as if blasted by the lightning flash'. And now I was entrusted with some of these devastating though priceless secrets. They consisted of the Hebrew alphabet, the names of the planets with their attribution to the days of the week, and the ten Sephiroth of the Cabbala. I had known it all for months; and, obviously, any schoolboy in the lower fourth could memorize the whole lecture in twenty-four hours.

But there was a justification. The whole grade structure encapsulated the Western Hermetic Tradition and the lectures were an integral part of the whole Golden Dawn system, as Brodie-Innes made clear in his Notes on the First Knowledge Lecture that were issued in 1895:

> The newly initiated brother of our Order, receiving the First Knowledge Lecture, experiences an involuntary feeling of disappointment – 'Is this all?' he will say to himself, 'After all the promises, the elaborate ritual, the pledges of inviolable secrecy. A few symbols to be found in scores of books.' But let him take heart. It is not to jest with him that this lecture is put forth in this way. Our curriculum is an elaborate system of occult education and training, designed many centuries ago, to lead men step by step to the highest advance they are capable in this life of attaining, and to the diligent student we can promise the unfolding of the Spiritual Life, the development of all the faculties, and the power to fulfil the purpose of this present earth life and to enter with confidence on the future.

I who write these few words have myself been a student of

63

the Order for near on 30 years, and I can say with absolute truth and conviction I would not be without one atom of the teaching I have had. Nor do I regret one hour spent in the study of its learning. Let him therefore not be discouraged at the outset. This First Knowledge Lecture indicates the plan and scope of his first studies and gives him as it were the alphabet of the sciences he is to learn. And this alphabet must not merely be known, it must be as familiar to him as the letters of the English alphabet.

The truth of which comments even Crowley recognised in time:

I see today that my intellectual snobbery was shallow and stupid. It is vitally necessary to drill the aspirant in the groundwork. He must be absolutely familiar with the terminology and theory of Magick from a strictly intellectual standpoint.

The real test of the initiate's progress came much later, when he entered the Second Order. Throughout the cere-monies of the Outer Order, similarities with masonic ritual (and even more so with that of the Societas Rosicruciana in Anglia) were clearly to be seen, but the workings of the R.R. at A.C. were of a very different kind and represented an entirely new depar-ture in the field of esoteric ritual. The structure and myth of the Second Order was based on the Rosicrucian Manifestos: the three anonymous pamphlets published early in the seventeenth century, that professed to set out the life and doctrines of the legendary Christian Rosencreutz, a fifteenth century adept who had supposedly travelled to the Middle East in search of wis-dom, had then returned to Germany and founded a secret Brotherhood of the Rosy Cross with the twin aims of healing the sick and of propagating Hermetic knowledge. It was the latter aim alone that concerned the R.R at A.C.

Before admission to the adept grades of the Second Order, the aspiring magician first went through the ceremony of 'The Portal of the Vault of the Adepts', which symbolised, in kabbal-istic terms, the Veil of Paroketh that lay between the Yetziratic and Briatic Worlds. It was itself an extremely complex ritual in

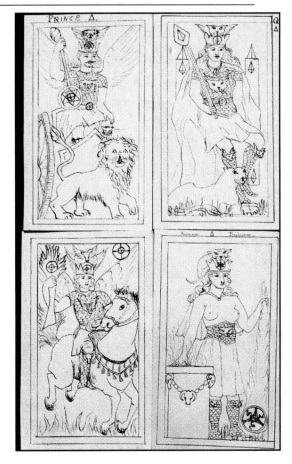

*Westcott designed the Court Cards for the Golden Dawn Tarot. The cards shown here (clockwise from the top left) are: the Prince/King, Queen, Princess/Knave and Knight of Wands.*

four parts, involving an extension of the kabbalistic, alchemical and Tarot symbolism with which the candidate was already familiar. Once the Portal had been attained, the candidate for advancement was loaned a book of 'Adept Addresses' which indicated the ideals expected of him; if he felt unable to live up to them then he was at liberty to withdraw. But few, if any, chose not to proceed.

The 'Ceremony of the 5 = 6 Grade of Adeptus Minor' was quite unlike anything that the candidate had experienced before. It was a second initiation, not a mere progression, and it involved the symbolic death and resurrection of the candidate. For the first of its three parts, or Points, the candidate was symbolically bound upon the 'Cross of Suffering' and there took his

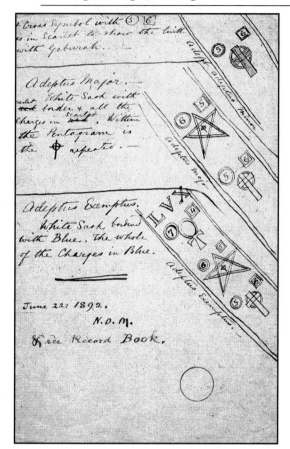

*Each member of the Order was required to wear a sash with insignia appropriate to his or her grade. The designs in this example, for Second Order sashes, were made in 1892 by Westcott (Non Omnis Moriar).*

Obligation – which was a far more awe-inspiring affair than that of the Neophyte; it bound the adept to strict secrecy and to the dedicated practice of magic and occult study; all in the presence of 'the Divine One, and of the Great Avenging Angel HUA'. The legend of Christian Rosencreutz was then related to him, as far as the discovery of his tomb – at which point a curtain was drawn back and the door of a seven-sided vault was revealed.

The vault was some 12 feet across, roofed, and with panels of eight feet by five feet, each of which was divided into 40 squares, each bearing a different symbol and painted in appropriate colours. Inside the vault was an elaborately painted pastos (or coffin), surmounted by a movable circular altar inscribed with the Hebrew letter Shin and the symbols of the four Cherubim of Ezekiel.

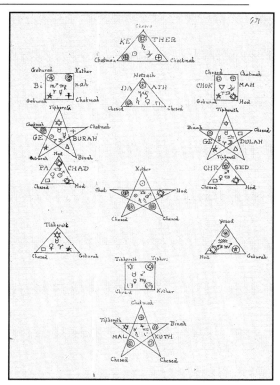

*Diagram from Ayton's transcript of 'The Lecture on the Lineal Forms of the Names of the Sephiroth in the Tree of Life', designed for 'such Zelatores Adepti Minores as have mastered the Pentagram & Hexagram Rituals; & consecrated their Magical weapons'.*

For the Second Point of the Ceremony, the Chief Adept, who represented Christian Rosencreutz, lay in the pastos with the lid closed, the altar placed over it and the door of the vault closed. The candidate (who had previously retired) re-entered and was shown the door of the vault, the symbolism of which was explained to him; the legend was continued, the door was opened and the candidate saw, for the first time, the painted interior of the vault, the symbolic Rose painted on the ceiling, the pastos and the altar. He reaffirmed his Obligation, the lid of the pastos was removed to reveal the Chief Adept – who then addressed the candidate – and the legend was completed. The Second and Third Adepts then replaced the lid of the pastos and left the vault with the candidate, closing it behind them.

For the Third Point the Chief Adept was released from the pastos, which was placed outside the vault, the altar remaining within. The candidate was led into the vault and addressed by the now resurrected Chief Adept, who then received him as a full Adeptus Minor and explained the symbolism of the grade to him in detail. The proceedings came to an end with the ceremonial closing, and the new Adeptus Minor was ready to begin his magical career.

It commenced with his acceptance of the prosaic 'General Orders' that concerned the organisation of the Second Order and the conduct of its members. The Adeptus Minor then proceeded through five stages, all of them involving a very considerable personal effort. In the first stage 12 rituals, including the Rituals of the Pentagram and Hexagram, for the invocation and banishing of assorted spirits, were learned and practised; ten 'Flying Rolls' were studied, and three examinations (involving the working of these rituals and the construction of magical implements with an understanding of their symbolism) had to be passed if he was to move on to the second and third stages. These involved the passing of three further examinations (on Spirit Vision and Astral Projection; Divination; and the making of Talismans), after studying 24 Flying Rolls and five more rituals. In the fourth stage, the Enochian system – the complex magical scheme developed by Dr Dee and Edward Kelley – was studied. This involved learning the Enochian Tablets, together with an understanding of their use in magical work: a dangerous process, as faulty working could result in spiritual obsession and psychological collapse. After this, the fifth stage with its ritual interpretation of the symbolism of the Neophyte Grade took the adept to a safe conclusion to his labours.

The Enochian system, bound up as it was with the concept of human interaction with superhuman beings, was central to the working of the Inner Order. It underlay all the activities of the Order from the consecration of the lotus wand, magical sword and the four elemental implements (Fire Wand, Water Cup, Air Dagger and Earth Pentacle) to the construction of the Rose Cross Lamen, the vibration of divine names and the construction of telesmatic images: images of letters and elemental forces in the form of talismans – usually visualised as angels. In addition there were such rarified activities as Enochian Chess, in which the boards were multi-coloured 'Flashing Tablets' and the pieces symbols of Egyptian god-forms; astral travelling; and a wealth of divinatory practices.

And then there were private magical practices, such as the working of the 'Sphere Group' which was formed by Florence Farr and was concerned principally with astral projection. Its structure was described by Annie Horniman who detested the group and thought the practice unhealthy and undesirable. She described the practice in a report in 1902:

> The group consisted of 12 members and the symbols were adapted from the Star Maps and Tree of Life projected on a sphere, whence they were sometimes called the sphere group. The twelve members had astral stations assigned to them around this sphere and a certain Egyptian astral form was supposed to occupy the centre.

Dr R.W. Felkin, who was a member of the group, saw it in a favourable light. Its objects were, he said:

> to concentrate forces of growth, progress and purification, every Sunday at noon, and the progress was 1st, the formulation of the twelve workers near but not in 36 [Blythe Road]; 2nd Formulation round London; 3rd Formulation round the Earth; 4th Formulation among the Constellations.

> Then gradually reverse the process, bringing the quintessence of the greater forces to the lesser. The process was to take about an hour.

Nonetheless, however noble their intent, such practices proved disruptive and led to increasing dissension in the post-Mathers era. They eventually led to a complete rift between the mystics and the magicians who made up the Golden Dawn. But new ceremonies for the Order were a different matter and dramatic innovations could be enjoyed by both factions. This symbolic burial came into use about 1905 and was certainly used by Dr Felkin's followers. It may also have been utilised by A.E. Waite. Perhaps they saw it as the final interment of the old Order and all its ways:

<u>Notes of Ceremony to be held on or about December 22</u>

Six Officers: Chief Adept, robed in white with black sash in form of Ankh round neck and waist; Second and Third Adepti in black robes with white Ankh sashes; all three carrying white Ankhs in left hands; four Bearers entirely in black with black veils over their heads. A bier lies on ground North and South. Candles on black pedestals stand in corners of room (Portal) no other light. Chief Adept kneeling before door of Vault, others form procession in ante-room; 2nd knocks six and three times. Chief replies with six and three. Procession enters, headed by 2nd and 3rd at rear; Chief makes farewell speech (Darkness of darkness – the people who sat in darkness & c). Procession circumambulates against Sun, ending with 2nd at North end of bier, 3rd at South, bearers at corners and other Adepti seated in West of Portal. Chief slowly rises, assisted by two bearers at N.E. and S.W. Makes speech, indicates desire on behalf of Second Order to symbolically enter into the shades that later on he may arise again as they all may if they fulfil their Obligation on the Cross. Assisted by two bearers he is laid upon the bier in a cross. Moving against The Sun, 2nd and 3rd change places; 2nd Adept speaks; then anoints Chief with oil in five places; retreats two paces, holds himself in the Cross and invokes Divine Name; 3rd comes forward from North to South, makes cross with ashes and returns to place. 2nd recites short form of committal invoking Supreme and Tablet Names to guard Chief in his sojourn in underworld; both circumambulate against The Sun round bier, ending 2nd at head and 3rd at foot. 3rd invokes Archangels. Two bearers N.E. and N.W. cross Chief's arms on breast; two bearers S.E. and S.W. give 2nd Adept water and 3rd Adept incense; they sprinkle and cense round Chief, then make Cross standing above him. Chief wrapped in robes and insignia placed in his hands by bearers. Bier raised by bearers, procession headed by 2nd, then bearers, then 3rd. They enter Vault saying 'I know that my Redeemer liveth' 2nd goes behind Candle in the E. Bearers place Chief in Pastos; light in Vault goes up; bearers stand at corners of Pastos, 3rd at foot; those outside murmur 'And that He shall stand & c.' 2nd takes up Candle; bearers place lid on Pastos, bring in Altar and put it in place; 2nd puts Candle on Altar, 3rd puts other implements in place; 2nd and 3rd sprinkle with water and ashes; 3rd goes to E. and both stand till bearers leave Vault, then 3rd, lastly

2nd leaves Vault and closes and bolts door. 2nd and 3rd stand either side of door reciting suffrages concluding with 'Go ye in peace, for know ye that as your servant hath departed in peace so by the power of the All-Supreme will he be raised again'. All file out with hands crossed on breasts and heads bent; 3rd first, 2nd last. After door has been closed 2nd knocks with six and three.

2nd returns and releases Chief who should not be again seen by other members that night. Final procession with The Sun. This ceremony should take place at 9 p.m.; Chief, 2nd and 3rd having fasted since noon, others since 6. The part of Chief should in this case be, if possible, taken by a woman.

So it was that even after Mathers had departed, his insistence on equality of the sexes remained. Even in symbolic death, the lady adepti were still emancipated.

# CHAPTER FOUR

# Lords of Misrule: the Masters of Magical Wisdom

## Woodman

Of the three founders of the Golden Dawn the most shadowy is Dr Woodman: not on account of any mystery in his life, but because he had the misfortune to die before the Order gained both fame and notoriety. He played no part in the creation of a working Second Order, and he had no foreknowledge of the troubles that would arise in the future.

William Robert Woodman had three principal occupations in life: medicine, Freemasonry and gardening, and he pursued all three with vigour. Born in 1828, he had become medically qualified by 1851 when he served as a volunteer surgeon during Napoleon III's *coup d'état*. He followed this stirring episode with a general practice at Stoke Newington and a role as police surgeon. Outside his professional life, gardening was Dr Woodman's great passion, and so highly was he thought of in gardening circles that the Royal Horticultural Society erected a memorial over his grave at Willesden. But his spiritual energies were directed into Freemasonry and the curious Orders that budded from it, especially into the Societas Rosicruciana in Anglia, to which he was admitted in October 1867, during the first few months of its existence. Almost immediately he was appointed Secretary-General, and when the society's journal, *The Rosicrucian,* appeared in July 1868 he acted as assistant editor under Robert Wentworth Little, the founder of the soci-

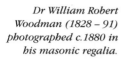

*Dr William Robert Woodman (1828 – 91) photographed c.1880 in his masonic regalia.*

ety and its first Supreme Magus (or Chief). Woodman held both posts until April 1878 when, on Little's death, he took over both journal and society. Little had already named Woodman as his successor. Under Woodman's control, the S.R.I.A. expanded and a kabbalistic emphasis was added to its studies – reflecting his own enthusiasms. In an obituary, Westcott later described Woodman as 'an excellent Hebrew scholar, and one of the few English masters of the Hebrew Kabalah'.

Both Westcott and Mathers came under his wing and he encouraged them in their own work both within and without the S.R.I.A., but we have no way of knowing just how closely he was involved in creating the Golden Dawn. Certainly he was capable of providing the specialised knowledge that was needed to build up the cipher rituals, but he probably held the position of Imperator of Isis-Urania in deference to his senior role in the S.R.I.A., for it is equally certain that he was neither as prolif-

73

*Woodman's letter donating his books to form the nucleus of a library for the Order.*

ic nor imaginative a writer as Westcott, nor a ritual genius in the mould of Mathers.

Nothing survives of any addresses he may have given to members of the Golden Dawn, although it is known that his style was rather ponderous. This is clear from his contributions to *The Rosicrucian* and to other S.R.I.A. publications. Its flavour can be judged from this extract from a brief paper on Freemasonry:

> In a future state of existence, when the soul has burst its bonds of clay, nor more entrammelled by its 'earthly tabernacle'; then, and then only we hope to attain nearer, and still nearer, to that mystic knowledge for which the soul is athirst – that soul, which immortal in its essence, and

emanating from the Deity, shall again resume its place amongst the highest of all created beings, and bask in those divine rays of truth and wisdom from whence it sprang.

Some of Woodman's early ideas may, however, have influenced Mathers if not Westcott:

> The Rosicrucians contended that these so 'poor in spirit', meant themselves and implied their abasement before God. Man was to have lived as the angels, of an impregnable, impassable vitality, taking his respiration, not by short snatches as it were, but as out of the great cup of the centuries. *He* was to be the spectator of nature – not nature *his* spectator. The real objects of the adept were, in truth, to remain no longer a slave to those things supposed to be *necessities*, but by the assistance of Heaven to remove back to Heaven's original intention; to rise superior to the consequences of the original Curse, and to tread under foot, in vindicating the purpose of God, that mortal (however seductive), sexual, distinctive degradation, entailing dissolution, heired from Adam, or from the first Transgression. That poverty, and celibacy (under certain limitations) must be the obligations of the true Brothers of the 'R.C.' will at once be seen from the above reasons, however wild and mistaken – barely even comprehensible. The original curse was entailed upon mankind by eating of 'the fruit
> Of that forbidden "tree", whose mortal taste
> Brought death into the world and all our woe.'
> The Logos or Word, the Divine Wisdom, Christ symbolised by the Cross, provided the only remedy, and therefore the Cross is the most precious emblem; it is the true *Talisman* to lift fallen man from his lost position, and raise his soul to that highest of all conceivable beatitude a reunion with the Father of All. (*Symbolism*, in *The Rosicrucian*, February 1873)

But in 1891 kabbalistic theory and the triumvirate of Chiefs alike came to an end. On 20 December, Woodman died, and the two remaining Chiefs divided up the spoils. Westcott became Supreme Magus of the S.R.I.A. and Mathers seized the Golden Dawn.

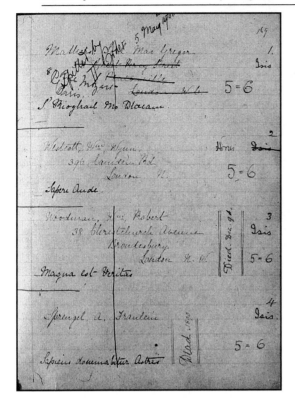

*The first page of the Golden Dawn's Address Book, showing the entries for Mathers, Westcott, Woodman and Anna Sprengel – Mathers' name was erased in 1900.*

## Westcott

Like Woodman, Westcott was a medical practitioner, but unlike Woodman – and for all that he was 'Dr Westcott' to his fellow occultists – he never obtained a doctorate, just as he never was many other things that he appeared to be. Westcott was born at Leamington on 17 December 1848. Everything else in his first essay in autobiography – a letter of March 1875 to F.G. Irwin, concerning entry into a 'Mystic Order' (probably the S.R.I.A.) – was exaggerated or falsified:

> William Wynn Westcott
> I am asked to state:
> My age Twenty-seven
> Place of Birth Landsdown Crescent, Leamington,
> Warwickshire

*Dr William Wynn Westcott (1843–1925), photographed in 1893 when he was Worshipful Master of the Masonic Lodge, Quatuor Coronati. This is how he appeared to members of the Golden Dawn during its heyday.*

Educated at Grammar School, Kingston-on-Thames and University College, London
Languages, English, French, & have some knowledge of Latin and Greek
Diplomas are Lic. Soc. Apothecaries – Member of College of Surgeons, England, and Degree, Batchelor of Medicine of University of London
My Principal Studies have been of course Anatomy of Man & Animals, & Physiology, Medicine, & Surgery. A little Mental Philosophy, Logic & Astronomy.

A conservative Liberal in politics, and in social life giving less appreciation to Birth than many others; believing that Education, Morality and culture give as high standing as the accidental advantage of Birth or fortune. (He had also been asked about 'All you care to reveal of your past life')

I hardly know anything of interest to reveal. Both parents died before I was ten years old & I was left to the care of my half uncle, an elderly bachelor surgeon, to whose practice I

77

have succeeded. Within a year of my beginning practice in this country town [Martock in Somerset], I was appointed as Manager of the National School & Representative at Diocesan Conferences. Also Manager of our Fire Brigade & cet. showing that I take an interest in the public good of my town. In medical practice I have no mishap. As a Freemason I prefer the ceremonies & try to limit the banquetting.

With regard to occult science – I desire knowledge & I am always pleased to obtain information. I know that what is called Mesmerism is a fact to some extent, & on a few persons I have been able to obtain effects myself; and I believe that when freed from imposture, valuable effects may be produced by it.

I am a member of the Church of England. As to amusements, I prefer scientific ones such as Chess; or Billiards which I play a little. And when I say that I abhor betting, sensuality and excess in liquor, I think I have mentioned all that may be necessary.

Westcott implied (as he did in later life) that he was an only child, whereas he was in fact the youngest of six children. One boy died in infancy, but all the other boys and two girls moved to Martock after their father's death. Westcott was never manager of the Martock Fire Brigade and did not manage the National Schools. Nor was the '& cet.' anything but a sin of commission, for it referred to his being the local Medical Officer of Health, a post he later claimed to have held but which in fact was in the hands of a prominent local physician, Dr J.D. Adams.

While at Martock, Westcott did marry. His wife, Elizabeth Burnett, maintained a sturdy and life-long disinterest in his occult pursuits. Richard Westcott Martyn, the elderly bachelor uncle, died in 1879 and the funeral seems to have been the last occasion on which Westcott accompanied his brother Richard. They never met again and Westcott never referred to him in any of his innumerable letters – not even to acknowledge his death in 1913. Nor did he mention his sisters, both of whom had died at Martock, one in 1872 and the other in 1907. Perhaps to escape from his uncongenial family, Westcott gave up his medical practice at Martock and moved with his wife and three children to London, where he 'went into retirement at Hendon for two years, which were entirely devoted to the study of Kabbalistic philosophy, the works of the Hermetic writers, and the remains of the alchemists and Rosicrucians'. He yet managed to father another son and daughter and to emerge from his retreat often enough to join the S.R.I.A. and to become an active member.

His time had been put to good use – studying Eliphas Lévi and preparing the exquisite pen facsimile that was to be used to illustrate his *Isiac Tablet of Cardinal Bembo* in 1887. Nor, as a good Rosicrucian, did he neglect his medical duties; he worked with W.H. Martindale on *The Extra Pharmacopoeia of Unofficial Drugs,* became Deputy Coroner for Central Middlesex and Central London – following this up in 1894 by his appointment as Coroner for North East London – took his Diploma in Public Health and began work on his medical magnum opus, *Suicide: its History, Literature, Jurisprudence, Causation and Prevention.* Many years after its publication in 1885, suicide became one of the many misfortunes that dogged Westcott's footsteps through his life, for in 1918 his second daughter killed herself. Only one child, his eldest daughter, survived him. His two sons died shortly after each other in 1906 and 1907 while his youngest daughter died unexpectedly in 1924 at her home in South Africa where Westcott had gone to live. Most harrowing of all was the death of his wife who fell from a hotel window in Tunbridge Wells, where they were staying prior to their return to South Africa in 1921. But when the Golden Dawn came into his life these tragedies were far in the future.

For ten years Westcott was content to play second fiddle to Mathers in the affairs of the Golden Dawn – from 1892 onwards he was responsible for administering the S.R.I.A. He had no desire to be burdened with the management of its more troublesome relative – but the ultimatum from the authorities in 1897 sowed the seeds of suspicion. It was not the first time that he had been so admonished. When writing to Gardner about

---

**The Hermetic Society for July, 1886.**

*Thursday 8th*, 8.30—The Physical Alchemy, by Mr. S. LIDDELL M. MATHERS.

*Thursday 15th*, 4.30—The New Illumination, by the HON. SECRETARY.

*Thursday 22nd*, 8.30—By the PRESIDENT.

*Thursday 29th*, 4.30—The Sepher Jetzirah, a Rabbinical Treatise on Creation, by Dr. W. WYNN WESTCOTT.

EDWARD MAITLAND, *Hon. Sec.*

22, ALBEMARLE STREET. W.

*See over*

---

*Programme card for The Hermetic Society, 1886. Both Mathers and Westcott delivered lectures – as did the Society's President, Anna Kingsford, who had earlier edited Valentine Weigel's* Astrology Theologised. *On the title page of this book appears the motto 'Sapiens Dominabitur Astris' which Westcott would later attribute to another Anna: the mythical Anna Sprengel.*

official disapproval of his 'foolish posturing' he referred to having received:

> a similar intimation in 1889 about the T.S. and my support of Madame Blav[atsky] at Avenue Road. and then I had to cease lecturing there on Thursdays. I was then Vice Pres. of Blav. Lodge. It looks as if someone was trying to get me out of GD office – eh?

'I hope', he added, 'to continue giving private help to members, unless M. takes it in an angry way, as to the trouble it gives him', suggesting that he was well aware of possible hostility on Mathers' part.

To protect himself from future accusations he obtained a statement from Theresa O'Connell (whom Mathers had expelled in 1893) as to the 'facts as I remember them [in 1898] connected with the refounding of the G.D. in England', and two affidavits concerning the receipt and translation of the Anna Sprengel letters and the preparation of replies. He received the affidavits from Alfred Essinger, a director of Westcott's Sanitary Wood Wool Company, and from Mark Rimmer, a clerk in their employ. Finally, in June 1900, after Mathers had written his damning letter to Florence Farr, Westcott obtained an affidavit from T.H. Pattinson of the Horus Temple at Bradford, which affirmed the status of the three co-equal Chiefs and commented on the personalities of the surviving two:

> I consider Mr Mathers' mental state to be a peculiar one, because he now claims the name of MacGregor to which he was not born, and also considers himself to be the Count of Glen Strae, which title is one of Jacobite nobility to which he never hinted any claim during the years when I saw most of him, and knew him intimately as a visitor in my own home.
>
> On the other hand Dr Westcott always was, and still is, a clear headed man of business and an earnest literary student, of whose character no suspicion has even been raised in the presence of myself or of my associates, except by this Mr Mathers aforesaid.

But for reasons which he never made clear – his excuses at the time were remarkably feeble – Westcott made no use of his affidavits and refused to defend himself against Mathers' charges. Had he rejected the accusations of forgery, and returned to play an active role with the Order, the whole furore would undoubtedly have blown over. Mathers, of necessity, would still have been rejected but the Golden Dawn itself would have remained intact. Why then did Westcott choose to remain silent?

Only two answers come to mind. One, that the charges were true, that Westcott had forged the letters – and thus by implication had falsfied the story of the cipher manuscripts as well. Against this Westcott had no defence, but could reasonably expect to receive the benefit of the doubt by saying nothing save to throw in a few red herrings such as his desire to protect Mrs Woodman. The other possible answer is that, regardless of whether the charges were true or not, Westcott was terrified that Mathers would make the whole scandal public and in so doing expose Westcott's cavalier attitude to the truth of his own professional attainments and thus jeopardise his masonic (and perhaps his medical) career.

He did, however, engage in a cautious campaign of character assassination against Mathers, as can be seen in his comments to W.B. Yeats and in a letter to Gardner in which Westcott appeared as the aggrieved innocent:

> Please accept best thanks for your services, in coming with Ayton's letter, for Ayton sent me his copy of a letter from Mathers about the new rebellion against his authority – it was marked 'not to be shown to anyone' and it threatened me with all sorts of pains and penalties for conspiring against him – which is very hard considering how I have kept away from all his pupils.

> He declines to close Isis and says the chiefs may all resign if they like. I have sent an answer to Ayton – as the oldest member – saying I can't interfere & that they ought to say to M. that I have *not interfered* with *him*. Allegations are easily made by M., a man of straw, which might cost me hundreds of pounds to refute, and that I must at present submit to his slanders.

> I have asked Ayton to send on the note *at once* to his friends the Acting Chiefs, with a request that they will not mix me up in their quarrels.

How they were to avoid mixing him up in the affair, since he was its prime cause, Westcott did not say: the rebellion proceeded and Westcott's brainchild fell to pieces – destroyed as much by his own timidity as by Mathers' paranoia. Sweet revenge, however, was not far off.

For ten years, Westcott suffered – or so it seemed – from Mathers' assault on his character. Then early in 1910, the tables were turned. Aleister Crowley had long since fallen out with Mathers and gone his own way, and in 1909 he began to publish a quirky occult periodical, *The Equinox,* which would have passed unnoticed save that it included the texts of the rituals of both the Golden Dawn and R.R. et A.C. for all the world to see. Mathers immediately sought – and obtained – an injunction restraining Crowley from publishing this copyright material; Crowley fought the injunction, won his case and Mathers retired hurt. But before this legal battle, Mathers had appealed to Westcott for help.

It was not unreasonable to expect such help, for the second number of *The Equinox* not only printed the Adeptus Minor ritual, but quoted from Mathers' letter to Florence Farr accusing Sapere Aude of forgery – adding in a footnote that 'S.A. was Sapere Aude (or Non Omnis Moriar), Dr W. Wynn Westcott, King's Coroner for Hoxton'. On 1 December, 1909, Brodie-Innes wrote to Westcott enclosing a cutting from the offending article and commenting (with some relish no doubt), 'Enclosed may interest or amuse you as a step in the career of a black-guard'. The letter went on to enlarge on Crowley's iniquity and in passing, to imply faults in Westcott's learning:

> M.'s solicitor tackled publisher & printer of The Equinox –
> both I understand disavowed any responsibility & said
> Crowley was proprietor & solely responsible. It is thought
> they will give an undertaking to print no more. Crowley has
> bolted & wrote to a friend from Pas de Calais that he was
> stony broke – this is a lie for his mother keeps him –
> however, probably he won't appear & an injunction will be
> granted against him in absence & so an end for the present.
> When he breaks that injunction (as he will) there will be
> 'wigs on the green.'

> Do you retain memory enough of the G.D. MSS. to answer
> this question? I have a very excellent copy of
> Schemahamphoresh which you had made for me – I know
> not from whence. On comparing it, which I have now done
> for the first time, with the Hebrew Bible, I find some of the
> texts are misquoted & so as possibly to vitiate the whole –
> e.g. the texts from the Psalms, where in the names of angels
> are drawn are said to be those containing [Yod/He/Vau/He].
> but in two or three instances this word is interpolated & is
> not in the original. Now is there accessible and Authorised
> Version of Schem Ham – or what is the explanation?

*The opening pages of Westcott's notebook in which he kept a record of his alleged dealings with Mathers in 1900. There is no independent evidence of the existence of the documents referred to in the notebook.*

May an old friend dare intrude on your learned leisure with such a query.

Westcott replied to Brodie-Innes at once, cleared away the Hebrew question and launched into the *Equinox* affair.

Private and Confidential

Best thanks for your letter. I believe Mathers drew up the Shemham lecture from British Museum researches, but I have no definite recollections – it is not a lecture I wrote.

As to Crowley. I am intensely annoyed that he should have printed the Rituals in his Equinox and I believe he must be a very bad man, and I wish he were banished for ever from this realm and planet. But as to legal proceedings, I think it would be wise to grin and bear it. Mathers as well as C. has enemies here who would be raked up to say unpleasant things in the witness box. Then M. as a ten years resident in Paris would have to deposit security for costs.

Remember that M. treated me in a very harsh fashion some years ago, and apart from the source of the G.D. knowledge, I am the only person who could prove he wrote the Rituals and so could claim the copyright. To get me as an amiable witness he would need to consider my feelings and position, and even then it would be very awkward for his case when counsel asked him·– is not W. the person you charged with forgery in these very Society matters? This must not be forgotten. It would be a very serious thing, for me as a J.P. and a Coroner to get brought in at all in a secret society case and I should want ample guarantees from him that he would safeguard my reputation, before I enter upon any preliminary correspondence even, upon these Society matters. He and you and I have all sworn to keep G.D. matters secret and I for one will not break my oath except by order of a Judge in Court.

Westcott evidently believed that Brodie-Innes was fishing on Mathers' behalf and he seems to have been correct, for Mathers approached him for help in securing an injunction. Declining to correspond directly, Westcott used Arthur Cadbury-Jones, the Secretary General of the S.R.I.A., as his go-between, explaining what he wished to do in a letter of 27 March, 1910:

I will leave Equinox 3 at your house tomorrow – I don't think you can have read the page which attacks me – it could only have been written when half crazy over the defection of his pupils – and as he wrote it, he says, from information given by a swindler he should have said subsequently he could not support his charges.

Ten years ago I got declarations from 2 witnesses that I had had translated German letters from S.D.A., & of course he knew about it – and accepted them as true so long as it served his purpose. He *may* still be fiery and malicious, so try *every smooth* means first to get the retraction – at any rate one of the present date, and one dated soon after December 23, 1900 also if possible. H[oros] was convicted Dec 20 – while M was in Paris.

After the slander by him of Feby 16, 1900, he made a contract never to speak again in my discredit & this was duly signed & sealed May 12, 1900, even before the Horos trial. The words are 'nor will Mathers attempt in any way to make any statements to his friends or the public derogatory to the position and standing of the aforesaid W.W.W. in the world.'

To go back to 1886–1887, I find I have two letters from him as to cipher mss. of Rev. A.F.A. Woodforde – in which he wishes to write up new rituals *from* them, that is as to the G.D. grades 0° to 4°. I have also a letter from M. to me from Bradford in 1888 in which he says he has told Pattinson about my correspondent 'SDA who is abroad'. How can he now honestly believe the letters were sham ones?

If he will do all I want I will give him a five pound note: don't let it look like bribery.

The next letter to Cadbury-Jones (probably sent on 30 March, although 1 April would have been more appropriate) was far more detailed and included the texts of three letters that Westcott expected Mathers to copy out in his own hand:

Dear Cadbury-Jones,

I am much obliged by your kind work on my behalf; please continue it, in case of further proceedings of any sort & of further quarrels by C. I think it best I should be able to say I have *not* seen M. on this occasion. My only hope for fair treatment lies in his desire for a money gift. His willingness to sign any form as to *my* starting the G.D. only confirms his own original letter – and is no boon, only a confirmation which I should consider proper from one who has broken every pledge of Brotherhood. The Second Order matter is really serious. I know M had said to some person he doubted whether my letters from Germany signed Sap. Dom. Ast. were or were not forgeries, but I did not know he had actually *written* and sent out such a charge of forgery, nor did I dream that Cr. had heard of the charge.

Crowley's quotation of Mathers' actual letter, saying I forged letters cannot be passed over. The charge may be repeated in any Daily paper & the London County Council may call on me to prosecute both M. for writing & C. for printing the libel, and I might be ruined; how could I rebut such a charge of what occurred in 1888 between me and a correspondent I knew nothing of? The only evidence on which he made such a charge was the statement of a prostitute adventuress as he confesses; he had to disown her and yet he has not sent me a withdrawal of the offensive charge. He has no other evidence and just because his own teacher Lux e Tenebris did not know that a person S.D.A. wrote to me he dares to say I forged the letters – it is intolerable.

If he wants a gift of money from me, he *must* write his withdrawal of the charge of forgery. He ought to write *two* – one a private letter to me dated December 1901, or early 1902, and a confirmation referring to the present row dated now.

I send you copies of what I should require – I am not going to give him money for nothing.

A lawyer tells me that I ought to go to a magistrate for a criminal libel against both M. & C. *at once*, before M. leaves; but I do not want to act roughly to one who was an old friend and fellow student. So here is an opportunity for you to use all your well known tact and acumen . . .

Do not say much to Mrs [Westcott] about C. & M., only about the Lawsuit not about the forgery charge. She returns tomorrow & she worries so over matters.

Don't let him see the pages in my handwriting. I send three drafts of what I propose to pay for. A and C could be typed & signed – B must be an autographed letter. It would be better to call him up on the phone or by letter and not write these things.

Yours sincerely,

Wynn Westcott

The enclosed drafts were all-embracing, exonerating Westcott and humiliating Mathers. He already knew the flaws in Westcott's argument. He had claimed that Westcott himself told him the letters were forged so that there was no real need to bring in Madame Horos. Westcott must have been a supreme optimist if he expected Mathers to do his bidding. The first draft (A) merely recounted the saga of the Golden Dawn and expressed Mathers' full acceptance of the traditional history of the Order. The others deserve to be read if only to indicate how devious Westcott could be.

Draft B: Dec 10, 1901

> Dear Sir and Bro. S.A., N.O.M.
>
> As you may be aware that some time since I sent a letter to one of a group of students of the R.R. et A.C. of which I am head, saying I feared you had forged some letters from one S.D.A. in Germany, I wish to say I can not now substantiate such a charge as made by M. Horos, who came to me with apparently good introduction. I find she is not a person who can be relied upon, in fact has been I hear, convicted of felony in London. With regret for the annoyance caused to you, I remain, yours,
>
> D.D.C.F. = S.R.M.D.
>
> S.L. MacGregor Mathers

Draft C: March 28, 1910

> Dear Dr Westcott,
>
> It is with great regret that I find that Mr Crowley in his Equinox has published a portion of a *private* letter from me – written on Feb 16, 1900, to one of my pupils, in which I said you must have forged letters from one S.D.A. in Germany.
>
> You will remember that my informant was discredited and indeed convicted of felony in 1901, and so my charge was withdrawn. I have done my best by an action at law to prevent this man from publishing his so-called revelations and I write to assure you that I make no charge of improper conduct by you, in relation to the Isis Temple of the G.D. of which you were the first member, or in respect of the R.R. et A.C. of which I am the Chief in England.
>
> Yours fraternally,
>
> S.R.M.D.
>
> D.D.C.F.
>
> MacGregor

There were no further dealings with either Mathers or Crowley but there had been an earlier brush with the Beast. In 1908 Crowley had tried to obtain access to the cipher manuscripts and had written an extraordinary letter to Westcott:

25.7.08
49 Rue Vavin,
Montparnasse,
Paris

Dear Sir and Brother,

I have received letters from a Mr Cadbury-Jones on your behalf. He omits to explain his intervention or to produce any proper authority; and in any case I cannot admit that the matter at issue can be settled by any third person.

Permit me to recapitulate:
1. You are or were in possession (or rather in charge) of the cipher MSS. on which the orders of R.R. et A.C. and G.D. were founded.
2. These orders were and are being exploited by swindlers and worse – I need only mention Madame Horos.
3. By preserving the secrecy & inaccessibility of these MSS. you render possible these crimes, and consequently make yourself their accomplice.
4. It is within my personal experience that the MSS. do contain, although in a hidden manner, the veritable formulae of initiation.
5. The guardianship of the honour of initiates has passed into my hands, and I am determined to vindicate it, and justify the confidence which has been placed in me, whatever the cost to myself or to others.
6. I therefore demand that you should make a clear statement of fact as to how the MSS. came into your hands, and that the MSS. themselves, prefaced by such statement, should be deposited with the Trustees of the British Museum. Or, if you have parted with them, that you should inform me how and when; and to whom you have entrusted them.
7. Thus I trust both to establish their authenticity
8. And to secure the knowledge for genuine students.
9. Failing this, I intend to publish a complete statement of the whole transaction from the day of Sapiens Dominabitur

Astris unto now, as I may best establish it from the documents in my possession and the witnesses at my disposal. I shall do this entirely without malice, with strict truthfulness, and with the intention of enlightening the general body of students, both as to the existence of the true formulae, and as to the vile uses to which even they may be prostituted. I shall give you then as now every opportunity of presenting your own side of the case, not only as to the matters now in dispute between us, but as to the forgeries of which your colleague has accused you.

10. If this course of action be displeasing to you, you will only have yourself to blame. I play fair, with all my cards on the table; I have no personal feeling whatever in the matter, or anything to gain in any way.

It is because of (not in spite of) these circumstances that I am perfectly determined to have my own way in this matter. And in order that Non Omnis Moriar may perceive that I do not write without authority, I have caused this letter to be supervised and approved by those whom he must recognise and to whom he must bow, unless his grade of $7° = 4°$ is even more nominal than has hitherto been supposed.

I am, dear Sir and Brother,

Yours very truly,

Aleister Crowley

[The letter is also sealed with two of Crowley's own seals]

Westcott made no reply to the letter and a month later received a brief note from Crowley, which read:

Sir and dear Brother,

I am commanded to say to you: 'The feet of the young men are at the door, and shall carry thee out'

Yours faithfully and fraternally,

Aleister Crowley

Nor was this all, for on 24 October, Crowley called upon Cadbury-Jones to harangue him about the cipher manuscripts and to try to pump him for information about Westcott's relations with Mathers. Cadbury-Jones gave away nothing and reminded Crowley that 'his reference in a previous work, [*Konx Om Pax*] to Dr Waistcoat and his 40 thieves was sufficiently offensive. Then he corrected me and said "it was not 40 thieves but 40 liars", which I told him was worse'. Within a year G.D. rituals and the charge of forgery were in print. Westcott had learned the hard way that Crowley was in deadly earnest – but at least he had been warned, and in a roundabout way he tried to warn Mathers via Dr Berridge to whom he wrote three days after Cadbury-Jones' interview:

> Dear Dr,
>
> A man named Crowley keeps writing to me for information re G.D. which I refuse. I know nothing of him, except that I once saw him about seven years ago. Was he admitted to G.D. in Isis Temple, or after the split? I hear that Mathers made him a dear friend – is he so still, or an enemy? I suppose he took the oath of secrecy like all others, but I am told he does not keep it, and wants to print a book exposing it.
>
> Can you give me any information? Are you and M. now friendly and what is his address?
>
> Yours truly
>
> W.W. Westcott

All of which information Westcott already had, but as a skilful manipulator of those around him, he knew the letter would go on to Mathers and having alarmed him would set him in the right frame of mind to provide Westcott with the vindication he sought. He could not know that his efforts would fail and when negotiations with Mathers opened he played yet another card. He instructed Cadbury-Jones to say to Mathers that 'you have seen M's own letter to W of 1887 & the contract of 1900 in which Dr W as a free gift gives up his rights in G.D. to M. in exchange for promise from M. to defend him.' It is doubtful if either letter or contract existed outside Westcott's fertile imagination.

Perhaps he believed them to exist on some exalted astral plane; certainly he trusted in the magical world – even placing his faith in divination when applying for the office of Coroner of N.E. London in 1894. This exercise he recorded:

> **May 28, 1894**
>
> Tarot Divination taken by S.A. 9 p.m., alone at home.
> S.A. decided to take Part One of the Opening of the Key, & to consider that if significator fell into • (Hebrew He) final it would be best to gain Coroners Office which is comparative wealth. It did so fall.
> The significator is Knight, King of Cups. The • (Hebrew He) final packet was then judged to show the present opinion of the County Council who are the Electors.
> Whole pack shuffled and self found and 3 on each side of me taken for opinion of selective Committee. Whole pack shuffled and self found and taken with 6 each side of me – to show vote of Council.
> Whole pack shuffled, and one each side of me taken. the 3 to show final result.

Westcott does not give the result, but it was presumably favourable as he was duly appointed Coroner. Would that life were so certain today.

After 1910 the Golden Dawn played no further part in Westcott's life, although he remained well-informed of all its doings from Gardner, Blackden, Felkin and Waite (until 1914, when Waite left the S.R.I.A. in high dudgeon). All his private Golden Dawn papers were left in the care of trusted members, in his famous 'black box'. When it was eventually opened, it contained none of the documents on Mathers that Westcott had claimed to possess. One can only assume that when he died at Durban, in Natal, on 30 July, 1925, those strange documents dematerialised and went with him into the spiritual world.

# Mathers

*Samuel Liddell Mathers in 1889.*

If little is known of the early life of Woodman and Westcott (and much of that little is misinformation), even less is known of Mathers. There is a biographical note about him among Westcott's papers; it is scarcely unbiased but the account of Mathers' outer life is more or less accurate:

Samuel Liddell Mathers

Son of William M. Mathers, a commercial clerk; his mother was a Miss Collins. He was born at 11 De Beauvoir Place, Hackney, on Jany 8, 1854. His father died early, and he lived some years with his widowed mother at Bournemouth until her death in 1885. He was initiated in the Hengist Lodge in 1877 but never became a Lodge Master. While in Bournemouth his studies were directed to mystic ideas by an acquaintance with Frederick Holland, a deep student of Hebrew philosophy. He was admitted to the Rosicrucian Society of England, and so became associated with Dr Woodman the Magus of the Society and with Dr Westcott. He pursued his studies under their tuition, making considerable progress and proved so apt a pupil that he published a translation of Rosenroth's *'Kabalah Denudata'* a work which has run through several editions and gave him a recognised position in Occultism.

On the death of his mother, he was left in very poor circumstances, and removed himself to London where he lived in modest lodgings in Great Percy Street, King's Cross, enjoying the hospitality of Dr Westcott for many years. In 1890 he obtained the appointment of Curator to the Museum of the late Mr Frederick Horniman, M.P., at Forest Hill, which was subsequently given to the nation; in 1891 he was dismissed on account of a personal quarrel. While there he became acquainted with a Miss Mina Bergson a fellow student of Mr Horniman's daughter, a talented young artist of the Slade School. He was married to Miss Bergson at Chacombe Church, near Banbury by the Rev. W.A. Ayton, who was himself a prominent mystic student and researcher into Alchymy and a member of many occult societies; after whose death his extensive library was purchased by F. Leigh Gardner the author of Catalogues of Rosicrucian Books, Astrological Books and other works. Mr Gardner published at his own expense Mathers' edition of *'The Sacred Magic of Abramelin the Mage'.* The late Mr Redway published Mathers' magical work entitled *'The Key of Solomon the King'.*

To the Rosicrucian Society's Transactions he contributed essays on The Deity in Hebrew Letters; Rosicrucian Symbols; and Rosicrucian Ancients and their Zodiacal emblems; he became Celebrant of the London College and for some years was Secretary to the Society.

In 1891 the Mathers moved to Paris where he made extensive literary researches at the Librairie d'Arsenal, an institution notable for its richness in occult literature, and at the Musee Guimet whence he derived much knowledge of Oriental, ancient mystic knowledge. Mathers also published an English translation of a French military manual, an Essay on the Tarot Cards, and a volume of Poems.

During his residence in Paris he adopted the Scottish motto of 'S'Rioghail mo Dhream' – 'Royal is my tribe', and declared his succession to the Jacobite title of Count of Glen Strae which he alleged had been given to his ancestor by King

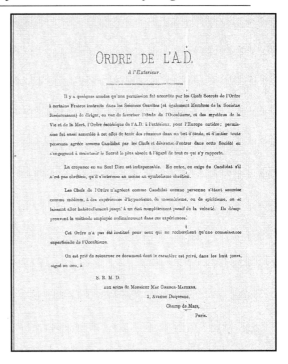

*The first page of the Pledge Form in French for potential members of the Abathoor Temple (c. 1894).*

James the Second. He was popularly known in the district of Auteuil as 'the mad Englishman'.

Owing to limited means he lost in Paris much of his reputation as a bona-fide student and teacher, and resorted to questionable practices which did not find favour in the eyes of his previous pupils. Mathers fell victim to the wiles of Madame Horos and her husband, two adventurers who were soon afterwards prosecuted and convicted in London of abominable offences. In Paris Mathers, also assisted by his wife, obtained an evanescent notoriety by an attempt to revive the worship of the Egyptian goddess Isis.

A pupil and dear friend of Mathers was Mr Aleister Crowley who subsequently quarrelled with and reviled his old teacher in several volumes of an eccentric periodical named *The Equinox;* in this publication, Crowley made public a great quantity of ritual instruction which he had received under promise of secrecy and this procedure led to an action at law which however was never satisfactorily terminated.

> During the last ten years, the Mathers cult has lapsed into well merited obscurity and we hear that he died in Paris on 20 November 1918 after a short illness from [influenza]. His irregular life in Paris and his overweening vanity led to his being deserted by his friends and supporters.

But not by all of them. This spiteful obituary was probably intended for the *Transactions* of the Metropolitan College of the S.R.I.A. but it was never published. His published obituaries tended to be gentler, even if they did not always praise Mathers. In the course of a long memoir in the *Occult Review* (April 1919), A.E. Waite remarked that Mathers 'had a natural faculty for suggesting in his mystery-language that he had a most profound acquaintance with any subject he took up, and it went a long way with the unversed'. This was a judgement based on Mathers' telling Waite that he had 'clothed myself with hieroglyphics as with a garment'. He yet seemed to have fascinated Waite, as he did almost all whom he met, and this lends credence to Waite's statement that Mathers possessed 'an utterly uncritical mind' and ' a fund of undigested learning'. He was seen in a similar light by W.B. Yeats who said of him that 'Mathers had much learning, but little scholarship, much imagination and imperfect taste, but if he made some incredible claim, some hackneyed joke, we would half consciously change claim, statement or joke, as though he were a figure in a play of our composition. He was a necessary extravagance . . .'

And what was the truth about him? Westcott had subtly altered a number of points in his obituary in order to emphasize Mathers' failings. He had known Mina Bergson long before he took up his post as assistant librarian to Annie Horniman's father. Mathers was never curator of the museum. Indeed, Mina was the first member to be admitted to the Golden Dawn after the three Chiefs, entering the Order in March 1888. There was no reference to Mathers' military obsessions – he was a private in the Hampshire Infantry Volunteers – or to his boxing and fencing. Not that Mathers always excelled at these manly sports; sometimes his poverty worked against him as Yeats recalled:

*Warrant of Osiris Temple.*

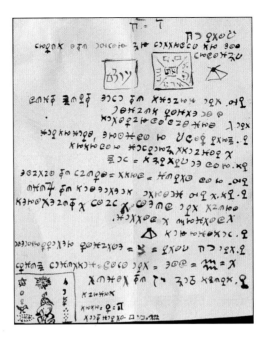

Above: *A leaf from the cipher manuscript.*

Below: *Rose and Cross symbols above the Obligation on the parchment Roll of the Second Order.*

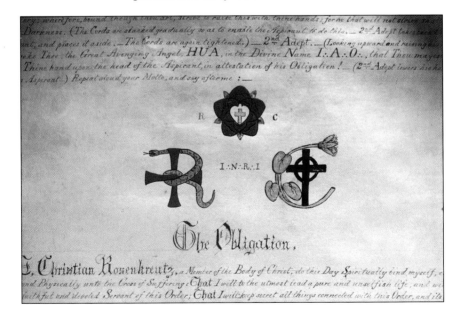

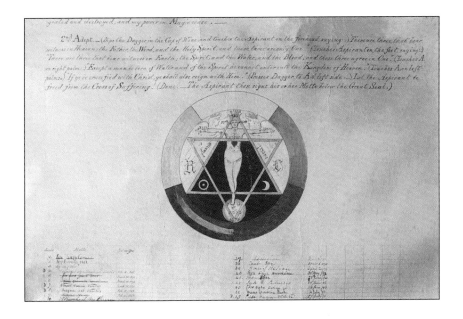

Above: *The Great Seal on the parchment Roll of the Second Order.*
Below: *Ayton's painting of a 'telesmatic angelic figure'.*

Above: *Designs by Mathers for the Lamens to be worn by officers when working the ceremonies of the Outer Order.*
Below: *The robe and regalia of the Imperator.*

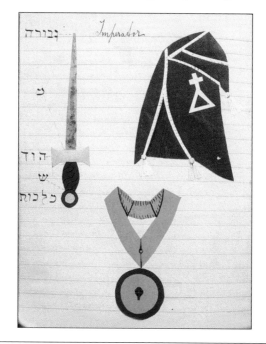

Above: *Second Order Regalia: the Rose-Croix Lamen of Benjamin Cox.*
Below: *Elemental Enochian Tablet of Fire.*

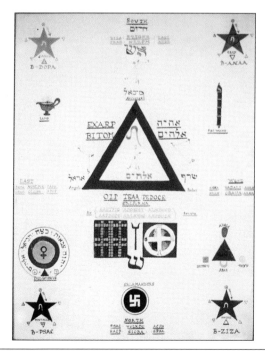

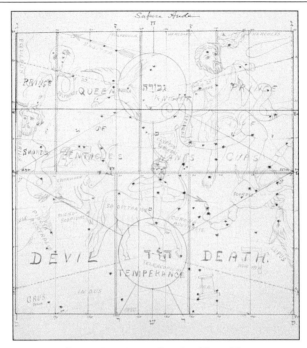

Above: *Star Map, showing Tarot Trumps.*
Below: *The Ring and Disk used by Westcott for Divination.*

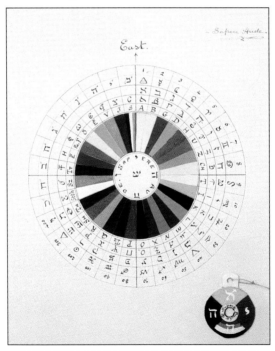

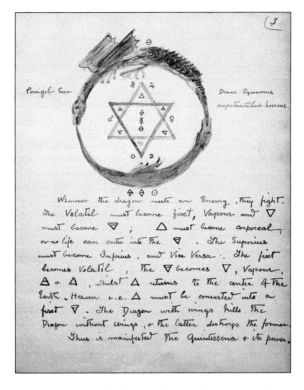

Above: *A drawing of the Orouboros (by Mina Mathers).*
Below: *Dr William Robert Woodman (1828–91), photographed with his family in the early 1880s.*

*'Golden Dawn' greetings card, issued after the Horos trial, front (above) and inside (below).*

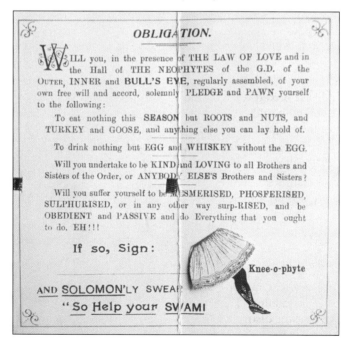

*Samuel Liddell MacGregor Mathers (1854–1918) in the uniform of a Lieutenant of the Volunteer or Militia Artillery (c.1882). In fact, he was never commissioned and does not seem to have risen above the rank of private in the First Hampshire Infantry Volunteers.*

One that boxed with him nightly told me that for many weeks, he could knock him down, though Mathers was the stronger man, and only knew long after that during these weeks Mathers had starved.

A.E. Waite in his autobiography *Shadows of Life and Thought*, recalled a fencing incident with a member of the Peel family:

> It happened that Mathers believed himself skilled highly in the art of fencing, so he had a friendly bout on one occasion with the man, and my acquaintance, in question. The House of Peel prevailed, and in the person of its particular scion was for ever disqualified as a Candidate for the G.D.

Mathers indeed took his enthusiasms seriously, but it was always magic that lay at the centre. In 1882 he was admitted to the S.R.I.A., took up Rosicrucianism with zeal, became within four years a member of the Society's High Council, and after Woodman's death in 1891 joined Westcott as one of the ruling triumvirate. He also gave stirring addresses to the members, as in 'Rosicrucianism, Deity, and the Hebrew Letters' which he delivered in 1885:

> Brothers of the Rosy Cross, ye are Brothers also of the Crucified Rose. That Rose is fadeless; that Cross is immortal it is the Rose of Creation; it is the Cross of Life! The Mystic Dew on the Rose of Sharon is the fructifying power of the Creative mind; and in the midst of the Rose is the form of the Supernal Man; we shall see Him, but not now; we shall behold Him, but not nigh; for He is the King of Hermetic Science, the Prince of the Creation of the Macrocosm; insupportable is His eternal Countenance, and with glittering glory doth it gleam. Know ye Him not, my Brothers? He is the Supreme Magus of Time, and the borders of His garment of flame sweep the ends of the Universe. Know ye His Name? It is the eternal Tetragram, the I.H.V.H.; it is the Name which rusheth into the Infinite Worlds. Spread are His Arms as to embrace the Universe, and on His Head is the Crown of Ages. And His voice is heard from the midst of the Cross, and it crieth aloud, 'Elohi! Elohi!' And lo! as He speaketh, on the arms of the Cross flame forth the letters of the Tetragram, and like the flashing of Lightning they rush and return, the four awful Cherubim of Light. And again His voice is heard from the midst of the Cross, and it crieth, 'It is finished.' And Earth is wrapt in Darkness amid the War of the Elements, and the Veil of the Temple is rent. But in the midst of the Darkness shines forth the Dawn, and it flames again in the splendour of Day. Who is She, clothed with the Glory of The Sun, with the Moon beneath Her feet and the Garland of the Zodiac on Her Brow? Her's is the Beauty of Endless Day. Know ye Her not my Brothers? Know ye only the Cross without the Rose. Rose and Lily of the Light of Time, Queen of the Limitless Spheres; Mother, Daughter and Bride of God, Crown Her with the Crown Divine. And behind Her again flameth the Cross, and She is Embraced by the Eternal Word; Supernal Woman, Supernal Man; we veil our faces and

adore. Whose is the Countenance Vast and Terrible, Shadowing over all? Who can know Him, my Brothers, who can know the Great Father? He is known of none, save those to whom I.H.V.H. will reveal Him. He is A.H.I.H., who hath said, 'I Am'.

This 'was listened to with the greatest attention', and it is doubtful if such fire and fury was heard by the staid masonic Rosicrucians before or since. All the flamboyance, energy and purple prose that would later go into the Golden Dawn were already overflowing from Mathers.

And as a practical magician, Mathers was superb. His magical prowess was recounted by W.B. Yeats who had observed Mathers at work more than once:

He gave me a cardboard symbol and I closed my eyes. Sight came slowly, there was not that sudden miracle as if the darkness had been cut with a knife, for that miracle is mostly a woman's privilege, but there rose before me mental images that I could not control: a desert and black Titan raising himself up by his two hands from the middle of a heap of ancient ruins. Mathers explained that I had seen a being of the order of Salamanders because he had shown me their symbol, but it was not necessary even to show the symbol, it would have been sufficient that he imagined it.

But the Golden Dawn – even the Second Order – brought no real satisfaction to Mathers. His poverty embittered him, as did his and Mina's dependence on Annie Horniman's charity to which he reacted by raging against his fellow magicians and by drifting ever closer to madness: the bizarre Manifesto of 1896 and the wild letters to Annie Horniman are evidence of an unhinged mind. In like manner he resented the continuing presence of Westcott within the Order. It was a constant reminder that Westcott, and not Mathers, had created the Golden Dawn. His petty actions against Westcott followed inevitably. Above all he felt deeply hurt by the world's refusal to treat his studies and his rituals in a serious manner. His magnum opus, *The Book of the Sacred Magic of Abra-Melin the Mage,*

*Mathers in the robes of the Hierophant Rameses performing the Rites of Isis in Paris.*

one of the few significant works on occultism to have been produced in the last hundred years, was remaindered – perhaps
because of poor marketing or possibly through fear on the part
of potential readers who could not have been reassured by one
of the concluding comments in Mathers' introduction:

> I will once more earnestly caution the Student against the
> dangerous automatic nature of certain of the magical squares
> of the Third Book; for if left carelessly about, they are very
> liable to obsess sensitive persons, children, or even animals.

To the world at large, who learned of them by way of the
Horos trial, the rituals of the Golden Dawn were an object of
derision and it could have no respect for their creator, however

learned he may be. Nor was the mundane world more sympathetic when it spoke French.

The Abra-Melin manuscript had been brought to Mathers' attention by 'my personal friend, the well-known French author, lecturer and poet, Jules Bois, whose attention has been for some time turned to occult subjects'. And it was Jules Bois who had dreamed up the 'Rites of Isis': readings from the Egyptian *Book of the Dead* (translated into French) with suitable 'Egyptian' costumes and dances designed for the occasion. For the public performances that commenced in 1898, at the *Théâtre Bodinière* in Paris, Mathers added his own invocations to Isis and he and Mina took the principal roles of Rameses and Anari in the ceremonies.

M. Bois introduced the Rites with an account of the legend of Isis and her worship and then the ceremonies began. The English public first learned of them through the columns of *The Sunday Chronicle* in March 1899, but a more entertaining account of an interview with Mathers and his wife, by Frederic Lees, appeared in *The Humanitarian* for February 1900:

> I was examining the curious green-stone lamp more closely when a voice at my elbow dragged me from my thoughts. It was the Hierophant Rameses who spoke. By his side stood his wife, the High Priestess Anari.
>
> 'I see you admire the Thibetan lamp,' he said. He proceeded with the enthusiasm of a true archaeologist to tell me its history. 'A beautiful symbol!' he exclaimed. 'It was brought from Lhassa, the Sacred City. Note that its three sides are not perfectly straight, that it is boat-shaped and flame-shaped. This lamp is symbolical, like everything else in our beautiful religion. Nothing that you can see here is without its meaning, nothing is without it's purpose. For instance, here is a sistrum shaken during our ceremonies. One side of the wooden body of this instrument represents the Beginning, the Alpha; the other side the End, the Omega; the metal part symbolises the Arch of Heaven; the four metal bars are the four elements. You will notice that on each of these bars are five rings, which, being shaken, represent the shaking of the forces of nature by or through the influence of the divine spirit of life. It is the same with our dress, as I will explain to

you after a while. And now let us go into the other room, where we can sit and talk at our ease.'

Five minutes later the Count and Countess MacGregor, of Glenstrae, were telling me of how they had come to revive in Paris, the worship of Isis . . .

'You have asked me,' said the Hierophant Rameses, the name under which Count MacGregor, who is a Scotch gentleman of fortune, appears in the Isis masses which he celebrates at his house in the Rue Mozart, at Passy, one of the fashionable suburbs of Paris; 'how we came to revive this ancient religion. The answer is simple. During our studies of the Egyptian religion we obtained certain lost truths, in possession of which we became converts to Isis. The revival, you see, was purely a private matter at first; we had not the slightest intention of making outer converts until an incident occurred which changed our intentions completely. But before I tell you of the incident, let me say one thing. Many have looked upon our propaganda with suspicion, under the impression that we are endeavouring to revive the worship of Isis as practised in its decadence. Now, this is far from our object. We have gone much further back than that; we have gone back to a time when Isis worship was in its primitive form, when it was not overlaid with growths as at later periods in the history of the world. Our Isis worship is Isis worship in its purest form.'

The rest of the interview was with Mina, and very revealing it is. But Mathers was not wedded to Isis to the extent that Mr Lees believed him to be. The early months of 1900 were the time of the great rebellion and it was a quite different Mathers who concerned himself with that. The manic tones of his inflammatory letters to Yeats, Florence Farr and Percy Bullock show a different man. They reveal the Magus at bay, his authority threatened by those he saw as moral and magical pygmies. And for them his tone would not change. In July 1902, he wrote to the 'Rebels against my authority in the R.R. et A.C. and in the G.D.' commanding them to 'abstain utterly from arrogation to yourselves of any authority soever in, or control soever over, either the Order of the R.R. et A.C. of the G.D., or of the Egyptian Mysteries'. He added the last item perhaps, because he

*After the Rebellion, Mathers continued to act as if the Order was still flourishing under his control. His own revised Pledge Form which he printed himself was issued at the end of 1900.*

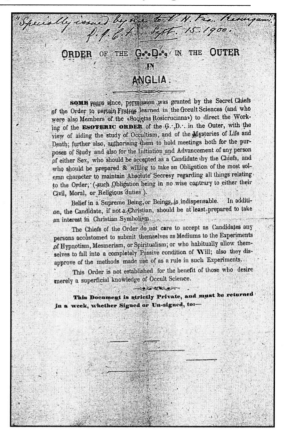

ORDER OF THE G∴D∴ IN THE OUTER

IN

ANGLIA.

SOME years since, permission was granted by the Secret Chiefs of the Order to certain Fratres learned in the Occult Sciences (and who were also Members of the Societas Rosicruciana») to direct the Working of the ESOTERIC ORDER of the G∴D∴ in the Outer, with the view of aiding the study of Occultism, and of the Mysteries of Life and Death; further also, authorising them to hold meetings both for the purposes of Study and also for the Initiation and Advancement of any person of either Sex, who should be accepted as a Candidate by the Chiefs, and who should be prepared & willing to take an Obligation of the most solemn character to maintain Absolute Secresy regarding all things relating to the Order; (such Obligation being in no wise contrary to either their Civil, Moral, or Religious duties ).

Belief in a Supreme Being, or Beings, is indispensable. In addition, the Candidate, if not a Christian, should be at least prepared to take an interest in Christian Symbolism.

The Chiefs of the Order do not care to accept as Candidates any persons accustomed to submit themselves as Mediums to the Experiments of Hypnotism, Mesmerism, or Spiritualism; or who habitually allow themselves to fall into a completely Passive condition of Will; also they disapprove of the methods made use of as a rule in such Experiments.

This Order is not established for the benefit of those who desire merely a superficial knowledge of Occult Science.

This Document is strictly Private, and must be returned in a week, whether Signed or Un-signed, to:—

feared that they had designs on the Worship of Isis. He went on to abuse them roundly:

> Your conduct from beginning to end is unspeakable in its vile ingratitude to me, aggravated as it is by deceit, lying reports, slander, libel and insult. It would seem that you have recoiled from no baseness.

Nor, when it suited him, did Mathers. He had been finally levered out of the S.R.I.A. in 1902 having attended no meetings since 1893, but he had always remained distantly in touch – if only to touch the society for money. In March 1901 he borrowed £10 which was never paid back, another contributing factor to his expulsion. As Christmas approached he sought a further £10 from Frederick Holland, the cynical Rosicrucian who had first drawn him into the Society:

> I am now writing to ask you a favour, which you may or may not care to grant. It is this: can you lend me £10? I could not possibly repay it for some months, and as it is I am still owing the Soc. Ros. some which they advanced me at the beginning of the year. I have had *terrible* monetary trouble and loss of late; and am at my wits' end to find ready money. If you cannot lend me the ten pounds or less, please send me a postcard by return with 'impossible' on it so as not to keep me in suspense.

It was a distressing letter to receive and, doubtless, even more distressing to send. But it was signed 'Comte MacGregor de Glenstrae'. Holland had no time for Mathers' Celtic pretensions. Referring to the 'Glenstrae' claim in a letter to Westcott of 1910, Holland commented that Mathers 'never mentioned such tosh to me and knew better than to do so, for I should have laughed him out of court'. In all probability Mathers received nothing, but somehow he survived.

What became of his magical activities in his last years is unclear. Some of the old Golden Dawn members supported him, Berridge and, later, Brodie-Innes being the most significant. And his few temples survived, to continue in their activities under Mina's supervision after her husband's death in 1918.

Brodie-Innes had a genuine respect for him and it was this that impelled him to publish a eulogistic obituary in the *Occult Review*, as a counterbalance to Waite's reminiscences. Mathers, he said, was a great kabbalist and a great Egyptologist:

> When he arranged a Temple of Isis for the Paris Exhibition, an Egyptologist whose name is world-famous said 'MacGregor is a Pharaoh come back. All my life I have studied the dry bones; he has made them live'.

He concluded his obituary with a flourish:

> Dear, impulsive, hot-headed, warm-hearted Highlander, he

had all the defects and the qualities of his race; misunderstood, reviled, and revered, brave and loyal to the last, bearing no malice to any, scarcely even resenting the many baseless falsehoods freely circulated about him, I am glad of this opportunity to add this one little leaf to the wreath laid on the tomb of my friend.

Loyalty certainly, but utter mendacity too – for Brodie-Innes knew full well that the malicious, devious and resentful man he praised had not a drop of Highland blood in him and had been understood all too well by friends and enemies alike. Mathers stands as a truly great magician, but as a man, as a mortal, he falls.

# CHAPTER FIVE

# 'Any Person of either Sex': the Ladies of the Second Order

From the beginning, the Golden Dawn had been open to women, as Westcott made clear in his Historical Lecture: 'In older times as at the present day, women rose to high rank and attainments in the Secret knowledge of the Order'. He went on to list some from the past:

> History is by no means silent in respect of the success of women in occult researches; mention may be made of Pernelle, the wife and fellow worker of Nicholas Flamel, of Martin Bertheran, companion to the Baron Jean de Chatelet, who died about 1645, and of the widow lady (afterwards symbolised by him as Sophia – Heavenly Wisdom), fellow student and inspirer of Johann Georg Gichtel who died in 1700, famous as a Mystic Theosophist.

Nor was there any shortage of strong-willed and capable lady occultists within this latter-day Order, although they differed from each other to an even greater degree than did the three Chiefs. Among them were three who stood out from their companions.

## Mina Mathers

If one discounts the mythical Anna Sprengel, the first lady member of the Golden Dawn was Mina Bergson who entered the Isis-Urania Temple in March 1888 and appears as No. 5 on the Roll of the Order, having taken the motto of Vestigia Nulla Retrorsum (No traces behind). She was born in 1865, of Irish-

*Mina Mathers as the High Priestess Anari in the Rites of Isis.*

Jewish parents who had moved from Dublin to Paris, and being a talented artist, she was sent to London at the age of 15 to study at the Slade School of Fine Art. Here, in 1882, she met Annie Horniman and began a long and close friendship that was not disturbed until 1888 and the arrival of Mathers. Despite her telling Annie that Mathers was 'an interesting man whom she did *not* want to marry', they became engaged and on 16 June, 1890, were married at Chacombe in Oxfordshire by the Revd. W.A. Ayton, who had been appointed for the task because he, too, was a member of the Order (as were the witnesses: Mrs Ayton and John Brettle). It was to be a curious marriage.

At first – while Mathers held his post under Frederick

Horniman – they lived at Stent Lodge, Forest Hill, but with the onset of poverty they moved to rooms in central London and began to live on Annie Horniman's charity. She encouraged Mina to return to Paris to continue her art studies (and perhaps to be separated from Mathers) and offered to provide her with money. From then, as we have seen, the relationship between the two women changed. Not that Mina's relationship with Mathers was anything but curious; it was, on her part, one of complete subordination to him in all occult matters; and it was devoid of sex.

Mina's attitude is made clear in a letter to Annie of December 1895, in which she discusses the 'elemental or human sexual connection (which I think with all other sexual connections are *beastly*)'. Referring to the concept of incubi and succubi, she wrote:

> When I first heard of this theory it gave me a shock, but not such a horrible one as that which I had when I was young, about the human connection. Child or no, a natural thing should not upset one so. I remember that my horror of human beings for a while was so great that I could not look at my own mother without violent dislike – and loathing.
>
> I have always chosen as well as 'SRMD' to have nothing whatever to do with any sexual connection – we have both kept perfectly clean I know, as regards the human, the elemental, and any other thing whatever.
>
> I have tried, and I think succeeded, never to allow myself to think of any subject in that direction.

But her unconsummated marriage did not interfere with her intense loyalty to her husband.

In 1926, eight years after Mathers' death, Mina prepared a new preface for a reissue of his book, *The Kabbalah Unveiled,* and gave him all the credit and all the glory for the creation of the Golden Dawn:

> Simultaneously with the publication of the *Qabalah* in 1887, he received instructions from his occult teachers to prepare

what was eventually to become his esoteric school. In this
connection, were associated with him, the late Dr Woodman
and the late Dr Wynn-Westcott, both eminent Masons and
Qabalists. They, with my husband, held high Office in the
Societas Rosicruciana in Anglia, and other Masonic bodies.

. . . In 1888, after the publication of the *Qabalah Unveiled*,
my husband started the working of his esoteric school . . .

The general constitution of the teaching, the skeleton of the
work, was handed to him by his occult teachers, together
with a vast amount of oral instruction. The object of the
establishment of this school was similar to that of the
foundation in ancient times of centres for the Celebration of
the Mysteries. The literature of this school, with a few
exceptions, was written by my husband under the direction
of these teachers, based upon the ancient mysteries, chiefly
those of Egypt, Chaldea and Greece, and brought up to date
to suit the needs of our modern mentalities. It is a system
eminently suited to Western occultism, which a man can
follow while living the ordinary life of the world, given that
this is understood in its highest sense. Dr Woodman and Dr
Wynn-Westcott aided in the administrative side of this school
and its teaching to a certain extent.

She may be forgiven for this nonsense, so breathtaking is it
in its mendacity. And just as she was the first real woman to
enter the Golden Dawn, so she was the first to enter the Inner
Order, going through the Portal Ceremony on 10 September,
1889. Nor was she merely a nominal 5 = 6. Having worked
through the Outer Order offices in Isis-Urania, up to that of
Hierophant, she became Praemonstratrix of the newly founded
Ahathoor Temple in 1893 and worked diligently both as a ritual-
ist and as a teacher. Four of the Flying Rolls were her work, the
most important being No. XXXVI, 'On Skrying and Travelling in
the Spirit Vision', which was issued in 1897. Some of her own
astral travels were recorded by Israel Regardie, including an
account of a visit to the gnomes. After carrying out the correct
ritual procedure she found herself

In a volcanic district. No fire is to be seen, but the type of
land is volcanic. Hill and mountains, hot air, and sunny light.

Using a Pentacle, and calling on the Earth Names, I see before me a species of Angelic King Elemental. On testing him, I find that he gives me the Neophyte saluting Sign, and the Philosophus (Fire) Sign. He bows low to the symbols that I give him, and says that he is willing to show me some of the working of the plane. He has a beautiful face, somewhat of the Fire type, yet sweet in expression. He wears a Golden Crown, and a fiery red cloak, opening on to a yellow tunic, over which being a shirt of mail. In his right hand he bears a wand, the lower end or handle being shaped somewhat as the Pentacle implement, and the staff and upper end being as the Fire Wand. In his left hand (but this I do not clearly see) he bears a Fire Wand; I think that the right hand points upwards and the left downwards, and is a symbol to invoke forces. Little figures of the gnome type come at his call. When commanded some broke the rocky parts of the Mountain with pick-axes which they carry. Others appear to dig in the ground. In breaking off these rocky pieces, there fell away little bits of bright metal or copper. Some of these Gnomes collected the bits of metal and carried them away in little wallets slung by a baldrick from their shoulders. We followed them and came to some mountainous peaks. From these peaks issued some large and fierce, some hardly perceivable, fires. Into cauldrons or bowls placed above these fires, the collected pieces of metal were placed. I was told that this was a lengthy process, but asked that I might see the result of what appeared to be a gradual melting of this metal. I was then shown some bowls containing liquid gold, but not I imagine, very pure metal. I again followed my guide, the Angelic King Elemental Ruler, who gave his name as Atapa, and followed by some gnomes bearing the bowl of liquid gold, we came, after passing through many subterranean passages cut in the mountains, to a huge cavern of immense breadth and height. It was like a Palace cut out of the rock. We passed through rudely cut passages, until we reached a large central hall, at the end of which was a dais on which were seated the King and Queen, the courtier gnomes standing around.

This Hall seemed lighted by torches, and at intervals were roughly cut pillars. The Gnomes who accompanied us presented to the King and Queen their gold. These latter commanded the attendants to remove this to another apartment. I asked the King and Queen for a further explanation, and they, appointing substitutes in their absence, retired to an inner chamber which appeared more elevated than the rest. The architecture here seemed to be of a different kind. This small hall had several sides, each with a door, draped by a curtain. In the centre of the Hall was a large tripod receiver containing some of the liquid gold such as that we had brought with us. The King and Queen who had before worn the colours of Earth now donned, he the red and she the white garments. They then with their Earth-Fire Wands invoked and joined their wands over the Tripod. There appeared in the air above a figure such as Atapa, he who had brought me here. He, extending his wand, and invoking, caused to appear from each door a figure of a planetary or zodiacal nature. These each in turn held out his wand over the gold, using some sigil which I can but dimly follow. The gold each time appearing to undergo a change. When these last figures have retired again behind the curtains, the King and Queen used a species of ladle and compressed together the gold, making it into solid shapes and placing one of these at each of the curtained doors. Some gold still remained in the bowl. The King and Queen departed, and it seemed to me that I saw a figure again appear from behind each curtain and draw away the pieces of gold.

Perhaps the astral form of Annie Horniman, withdrawing her largesse? They were, indeed, far more dependent on Annie's generosity than they liked to admit, and as this ebbed and flowed, so did the tone of Mina's letters change. Thus in January 1896, she wrote in a friendly tone to hurry along the money:

My dear Fortiter [Fortiter et Recte – Annie's motto in the Order]

Thank you so very much for your kindness – We would prefer the quarterly payment, if the same to you. – Only we have just had to pay the rent & have but little left over, so that it would make it very difficult for us to wait till March. But if it would not inconvenience you for the quarterly payments to commence soon, it would be all right.

Your arrangement will suit us admirably & we thank you

again. We are so glad about 'Mens Cons' [Mens Conscia Recte; the motto of Francis Wright, who had previously fallen on hard times and had presumably recovered – a parallel Mina was doubtless keen to emphasize].

Vale! Yrs.

Vestigia


But as the gulf between Mathers and Annie widened, so the friendship with Mina evaporated, and in June 1900 – after the rebellion had become a *fait accompli* – Mina sent an angry, hostile letter that destroyed any hope of their remaining friends. At least, one assumes that Mina agreed with the contents of the letter, for it is written and signed on her behalf by Mathers, and from the arrogant and intemperate tone, it seems probable that he composed it:

To Miss Horniman

Madame

I have received your document etc.

In reference to my remaining a member of RR et AC, I do not recognise your right to question me on such a point, as I acknowledge no authority save that of The Secret Chiefs, represented now in the outer world by DDCF.

As for belonging to any society that you and your friends may have formed, that you choose to misname the R.R.A.C., I must decline to be so dishonored.

The whole knowledge, property & m.s. of the Order, since the death of Magna est Veritas were vested in D.D.C.F. & 'Sapere Aude'& therefore the action of your friends seems to me simply to be one of common thievery, added to perfidy & inconsistency.

Either the knowledge is great & some recognition is due to the giver, or it is worthless. In the latter case, why steal the mss. & properties?

Both DDCF & myself had pledged ourselves & made ourselves responsible for you, but now your evil Karma for which we have so long suffered has departed from us with your action & the time of your expiation is at hand.

'Vestigia Nulla Retrorsum'

87 Rue Mozart, Paris. 15 June, 1900

As the document in question was a printed form to be signed by members who accepted 'the authority of the elective Executive Council in place of the late Chief D.D.C.F.', the tone of the letter is understandable.

But for Mina there was still a life away from the Golden Dawn in the form of the Rites of Isis. She explained to Frederic Lees how they came about:

> 'It happened in this way', said the High Priestess Anari. 'We made the acquaintance of M. Jules Bois, who, being interested as you know in religions and religious revivals, asked us if we could give an Isiac ceremony at the Bodiniere Theatre. He had already lectured there on Buddhism, and arranged for a Buddhist Mass, so he thought it would interest the public to know something about Isis. But we were very much disinclined to appear in public. We refused, therefore, and the matter would have dropped but for the intervention of the goddess Isis herself. One night she appeared to me in a dream and sanctioned any efforts we might make in Paris, her ancient city. Our scruples were swept aside. That is how we came to appear at the Bodiniere, first, when M. Bois delivered a lecture on Egyptian Magic, and introduced us to the public, again when we celebrated masses there.'

She went on to explain the role of the priestess:

> 'The idea of the Priestess is at the root of all ancient beliefs', she said, on one occasion. 'Only in our ephemeral time has it been neglected. Even in the Old Testament we find the Priestess Deborah, and the New Testament tells us of the Prophetess Anne. What do we find in the modern development of religion to replace the feminine idea, and consequently the Priestess? When a religion symbolises the universe by a Divine Being, is it not illogical to omit woman, who is the principal half of it, since she is the principal creator of the other half – that is, man? How can we hope

that the world will become purer and less material when one excludes from the Divine, which is the highest ideal, that part of its nature which represents at one and the same time the faculty of receiving and that of giving – that is to say, love itself in its highest form – love the symbol of universal sympathy? That is where the magical power of woman is found. She finds here force in her alliance with the sympathetic energies of Nature. And what is Nature if it is not an assemblage of thoughts clothed with matter and ideas which seek to materialise themselves? What is this eternal attraction between ideas and matter? It is the secret of life. Have you ever realised that there does not exist a single flame without a special intelligence which animates it, or a single grain of sand to which an idea is not attached, the idea which formed it? It is these intelligent ideas which are the elementals, or spirits of Nature. Woman is the magician born of Nature by reason of her great natural sensibility, and of her instructive sympathy with such subtle energies as these intelligent inhabitants of the air, the earth, fire and water.'

This summed up the theory which lay beneath her astral travelling, but for Mr Lees, 'These words give a better idea than any of mine could, of the thoughtful and dreamy nature of the Countess MacGregor.'

Beneath them appears something mystical, occult; we catch the glint of a singular mind. This mysticism, this tendency towards the occult appears, moreover, in everything she undertakes. It is so in her speeches and in her writings. For the High Priestess Anari is an accomplished artist. A former student at Colarossi's, and at other Parisian academies, she has had a thoroughly good training in art. The methods which she acquired there she has applied in her own way, following no particular master, but relying entirely upon her own thoughts. Her work is, consequently, very original. Her men and women, and the objects which surround them, are not of this world, but of the world of the imagination, where in her opinion true beauty is only to be found

Not that there was much of beauty in the Golden Dawn after 1900, with its members in revolt and its temples in disarray. There was, too, the spectre of poverty, although never so terrifying as to justify Crowley's scurrilous tale of meeting Mina while on his honeymoon with Rose Kelly in Paris in 1903:

> Rose and I were walking towards the Pont Alexandre III when I met Vestigia, as we always called Mrs Mathers. I had not seen her for a long time and we started an animated conversation. I noticed nothing peculiar. I do not live in the world of phenomena: I only visit it at rare intervals. I had forgotten Rose's existence. When Vestigia had gone, I realised that I had not introduced her to my wife. She did not ask me who it was. I told her. 'Oh,' she said, 'I thought it was some model that you knew in the old days.'

> The words came as a terrific shock. Vestigia had been our ideal of refinement, purity, spirituality and the rest. And then my mind informed me of what my eyes had seen, that Vestigia was painted thickly to the eyes – did I say painted? I mean plastered. Where the camouflage stopped, there was a neck which could not have been washed for months. I learnt later that Mathers, falling upon evil times, had forced his wife to pose naked in one of the Montmartre shows which are put on for the benefit of ignorant and prurient people, especially provincials and English, and that even that was not the worst of it.

*(The Confessions of Aleister Crowley,* 1969, pp. 371–2)

However cruel and untrue, the story does point to one prominent trait in Mina's character – her complete subservience to her husband. In all their magical activities, she seems always to have been overshadowed by him, and even after he had died it was his system that was worked until her own death in July 1928, in the A. O. Lodge that she founded on her return to London. And yet she did have real magical ability, despite Dion Fortune's scornful account of the jealous mistress under whom she served her magical apprenticeship:

> It may be as well to explain my own position in relation to the 'Golden Dawn'. I joined the southern branch of the Scottish Section of it, since disbanded, in 1919, and transferred from there to the section of it of which Mrs

MacGregor Mathers was the head, and which claimed the only orthodoxy. She nearly turned me out for writing *The Esoteric Philosophy of Love and Marriage,* on the grounds that I was betraying the inner teaching of the Order, but it was pointed out to her that I had not then got the degree in which the teaching was given, and I was pardoned. She suspended me for some months for writing *Sane Occultism,* and finally turned me out because certain symbols had not appeared in my aura – a perfectly unanswerable charge. However, I transferred again to yet another section of the Order, where, for the first time, I saw justice done to what is, in my opinion, a very great system, and continued my studies without interruption.

The 'Fraternity of the Inner Light' was founded by me in agreement with Mrs Mathers, to be an Outer Court to the 'Golden Dawn' system. All went well at first, and I was in high favour; but presently I fell from grace; why, I never knew. No specific charges were ever made against me, save that of not having the proper symbols in my aura. Finally I was turned out without reason assigned, save the ridiculous one above. My experiences, when I persisted in using the Order system, I have related in *Psychic Self-Defence.* Unpleasant as those experiences were, the fact remains that Mrs Mathers' rejection of me did not close the gates of the Order to me on either the outer or the inner planes.

In *Psychic Self-Defence* the full story of the 'unpleasant experiences' is given. They involved cats:

'We became most desperately afflicted with black cats. They were not hallucinatory cats, for our neighbours shared in the affliction, and we exchanged commiserations with the caretaker next door who was engaged in pushing bunches of black cats off doorstep and window-sill with a broom, and declared he had never in his life seen so many, or such dreadful specimens. The whole house was filled with *the* horrible stench of the brutes.'

That this was not due to natural causes soon became clear when Dion Fortune 'suddenly saw, coming down the stairs towards me, a gigantic tabby cat, twice the size of a tiger. It appeared absolutely solid and tangible. I stared at it petrified for a second, and then it vanished. I instantly realised that it was a simulacrum, or thought-form that was being projected by someone with occult powers.' It was then a simple matter to dispose of this psychic invasion although Mina herself proved a more formidable opponent and was not vanquished until her erstwhile pupil had been first bested in an occult battle:

> She appeared to me in the full robes of her grade, which were very magnificent, and barred my entry, telling me that by virtue of her authority she forbade me to make use of these astral pathways. I replied that I did not admit her right to close the astral paths to me because she was personally offended, and that I appealed to the Inner Chiefs, to whom both she and I were responsible. Then ensued a battle of wills in which I experienced the sensation of being whirled through the air and falling from a great height and found myself back in my body. But my body was not where I had left it, but in a heap in the far corner of the room, which looked as if it had been bombed. By means of the well-known phenomenon of repercussion, the astral struggle had apparently communicated itself to the body, which had somersaulted round the room while an agitated group had rescued the furniture from its path.

Dion, of course, returned to the fray, decisively beat Mrs Mathers and, 'the fight was over. I have never had any trouble since'.

But not all of Mina's encounters at this time were hostile. In 1923 she once again met W.B. Yeats, although her pleasure at the meeting was marred by a subsequent reading of his autobiography, *The Trembling of the Veil*. As she expressed it, 'Your book pained me so much after the pleasure I had had in meeting you again. I suppose I was so pleased to see you that the past for the moment had receded.' This remark was made in a more friendly reply after Yeats had promised to make amends for the passages that provoked Mina's bitter letter of 5 January, 1924, in which she complained:

> I have read your 'Trembling of the Veil'. I had expected some kind

125

of shock, but not quite such a violent one as I have received. Had you limited your caricature portrait of S.R.M.D. to the years of your connection with him, I should not have cavilled greatly at your description notwithstanding your many inaccuracies and misunderstandings; for instance the passage relating to our War prognostications is incorrect and there are many other passages which contain only half truths.

After elaborating on these 'inaccuracies and misunderstandings' she concluded her letter by cutting him off:

Now with this awful book of yours between us, I can never meet you again or be connected with you in any way save you make such reparation as may lie in your power. If you sincerely regret some of the aforesaid misrepresentations as I gather from your conversation, you have done, could you not in some immediate future work, refute at least some of the lying statements that must have been reported to you. You yourself may think of some other way.

As a perfect gentleman, Yeats did. All the offending passages were altered for *Autobiographies* (1926), and his one major esoteric work, the remarkable *A Vision* (1925), is dedicated 'To Vestigia'. 'Perhaps', he suggested,

this book has been written because a number of young men and women, you and I among the number, met nearly forty years ago in London and in Paris to discuss mystical philosophy. You with your beauty and your learning and your mysterious gifts were held by all in affection, and though, when the first draft of this dedication was written, I had not seen you for more than thirty years, nor knew where you were nor what you were doing, and though much had happened since we copied the Jewish Schemahamphorasch with its seventy-two Names of God in Hebrew characters, it was plain that I must dedicate my book to you.

For Yeats, if not for Mina herself, true beauty had been in her presence.

# Annie Horniman

If, in her later years, Annie Horniman had retained her persona of 'Soror Fortiter et Recte' and played the part of psychic bruiser in the magical battles against Dion Fortune, the imagery of the affair would have been wholly appropriate – for since her days at the Slade, she had been 'Tabbie' to Mina's 'Bergie'. But after the alarms and diversions of 1900 it could never have been.

Annie Elizabeth Frederika (to give her full name) was five years older than Mina, having been born on 3 October, 1860, the daughter of a wealthy and scholarly businessman, Frederick Horniman – famous equally as the founder of the Horniman Museum and as the importer and distributor of Mazawattee tea. Despite his fascination with ethnographical art and curious customs, and his involvement with Freemasonry, Annie's father had no apparent interest in occultism and it is far from clear how his daughter's interests arose. She was an independent child who rebelled against the social narrowness of her Quaker background. The most wicked things in the world were perceived by her family as playing cards and the theatre. She took to smoking, dancing and bicycling tours of the continent.

At the age of 21, she entered the Slade School of Art and over the course of five years discovered that she was not an artist, although she proved to be an excellent copyist. And at the Slade she acquired her nickname. A fellow student pointed out that viewed from behind, with her hair done up at the sides and looking like cat's ears, she seemed exactly like a cat. So it was that 'Tabbie' came into being.

It was, perhaps, her love of the theatre that brought her into the Golden Dawn as much as her friendship with Mina. She was not initiated until January 1890 and although she obtained Mathers his post with her father, she evidently did not like him. It had taken two years for her to come around to his brand of practical occultism. For all that she was close to Mina, she was not present at the wedding in June. As Mina was jealous of her husband's peers, so Annie was clearly jealous of Mathers, although she had become fascinated by the Order and accepted

*Annie Elizabeth Frederika Horniman (1860–1937), with Teddy-bear, on the occasion of receiving her honorary M.A. from Manchester University in 1910.*

Mathers' authority.

Her progress was somewhat lackadaisical: many years later she told A.E. Waite (as he noted in his record of 'testimonies' of various Second Order members) that 'she took the Neophyte Grade at Vestigia's studio in Fitzroy Street' and the 1 = 10 and 2 = 9 'in the sitting room at Fitzroy Street'. When her time came to enter the Second Order, 'S.A. showed Fortiter a single sheet of paper with a Diagram of Cruces Ansatae held over an altar. This was presumably before she entered the Second Order and at a time when it was in preparation only'.

The preparations were not straightforward, for: 'She was told, and apparently by S.A., that they "had much difficulty in translating the cipher" of the 5 = 6 Grades, because it was in alternate lines of English, French and Latin.'

*Annie Horniman's request for admission to the Second Order (December 1891).*

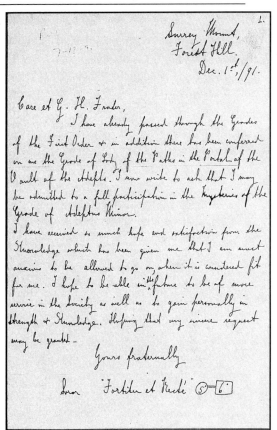

'In which case,' added Waite, sarcastically, 'it did not call for translation.' And Annie's statement throws further into confusion the question of just who worked on the Adeptus Minor ritual. She went on to tell Waite that: 'there was some red ink on the paper, meaning the sheet which contained the Diagram, and that S.A. did not say definitely that this was a copy of the cipher'.

Before taking the ceremony in the vault at Thavies Inn – where she 'was the first candidate to take it' – Annie (or Fortiter et Recte, as she was in this context) 'knew that they were making preparations with regard to the Inner Order', and Mathers 'gave her to understand that there were people above him'. They were evidently very retiring people, however, for 'D.D.C.F., Vestigia Nulla Retrorsum and S.A. took the Obligation from each other'. She concluded her remarks to Waite with the scarcely surprising remark that 'all the arrangements of both Orders were in confusion'.

Soon after Annie had attained the grade of Adeptus Minor, she went abroad and received 'the Hexagram and Pentagram Lectures at Florence soon after, together with a list of examinations in the Second Order'. She then went to Venice, where Mina joined her and talked enthusiastically of Mathers' military and political obsessions. Waite duly recorded her comments:

> She [Mina] had developed the Mars mania and had changed much. She gave Fortiter to understand that they were mixed up with politics and hinted that this would be the case with Fortiter herself in the future. Both she and DDCF were very anxious to bring Fortiter into their supposed political work, though they were not explicit about it.

Shortly afterwards Annie began to give them money and the Mathers moved to Paris.

Annie, as Fortiter, worked diligently within the Order, progressing through the Outer Order offices and acting as Sub-Praemonstratrix of Isis-Urania throughout 1895 and the first half of 1896. She went on Westcott's behalf to Bradford to reprove the insubordinate members of Horus Temple, and on 6 January, 1894, she consecrated the new Ahathoor Temple at Paris. In the words of the Minute Book of Ahathoor:

> V.H. Sor. Fortiter et Recte was sent by the Chiefs from London as their delegate to conduct the ceremony.
>
> The Temple was opened in the O = O by V.H. Sor Fortiter; who then read the Authority from the G.H. Chiefs of the Second Order empowering her to act as Consecrating Officer.
>
> She delivered a congratulatory Address on the opening of the Temple, which also pointed out the necessity for reverence and particularity in the actual working of the Ceremonies, as well as care in working up the knowledge of the various Grades.

After the Ceremony, at Mathers' suggestion, she was elected an honorary member of Ahathoor Temple – his spiritual *quid pro quo* for her worldly generosity.

Despite her enthusiasm for accurate knowledge of the subjects appropriate to each grade, Annie produced only one of the Flying Rolls, No. XVIII, on 'Progress in the Order'. This is a brief exhortation to Neophytes (and to new Adepti Minores) not to be discouraged; to overcome the anxieties and disappointments that follow admission to the Order. Recognising that new initiates are likely to be dumbfounded when faced with the need to keep inviolate such improbably 'secret' information as the Hebrew alphabet, she reassured them:

> If we look a little closer, however, it will appear only reasonable; we must be trained to be silent and perfectly discreet, so that secrecy will be no effort to us, when after much labour and many struggles we are gradually entrusted with the hidden knowledge belonging to the higher Grades of our Order.

She went on to encourage them in the face of 'a strong feeling of disinclination for study at convenient times', or of familial opposition and indifference. Those who had struggled through had gained much; but the aims of Order members must be of the right sort:

> To those who have made some little progress the true prosperity of our Order is very dear, and we look back with real gratitude to those who watched us until they thought fit, and then brought us in to what has become a great and important part of our lives. In some cases, it was an intimate friend, in others a comparative stranger whose acquaintance at first seemed to be of very little importance.

> Of course, we are often disappointed; when beginners ourselves we were most anxious for those dear to us to come in also, but as time goes on we see how rare are the qualities required and we find that we must have great patience and hope in regard to our friends, who as yet do not want to sympathise with our Hermetic aims.

131

Those who expect worldly or social gain for themselves
through this Order will be disappointed, yet none of us who
have made sacrifices for it in a right spirit are disappointed
with the result.

When this was written, in June 1893, Annie was far from
having to make any sacrifice herself. She could afford to fund
the Mathers as she had recently received a 'substantial legacy'
from her grandfather's estate. Some of the money she used to
back a season of plays at the Avenue Theatre, put on by
Florence Farr. They included Yeats' *The Land of Heart's Desire*
and Shaw's *Arms and the Man*, which ensured that the season
was a critical success although it remained a financial disaster.
Even so, it fired her latent enthusiasm for the theatre and paved
the way for the later founding of the Abbey Theatre in Dublin
and the Gaiety Theatre in Manchester. Her theatrical skill, coupled with that of Florence Farr, undoubtedly ensured spectacu-
lar workings of the Golden Dawn rituals when the two women
were, respectively, Sub-Praemonstratrix and Praemonstratrix of
Isis-Urania in 1895 and 1896.

There were, however, problems to be overcome. Not all of
Annie's disputes with Mathers concerned money. He was also
irritated by her vociferous objections to the allegedly 'impure'
sexual notions put about by Dr Berridge – in his persona of
Frater Resurgam. Annie was not alone in objecting to Berridge.
Mrs Rand wrote to Mathers to tell him 'that when I was a $4 = 7$
Resurgam after giving me instruction in astrology, attempted to
kiss me, and I was obliged literally to turn him out of the house,
so that I have personal experience of his possible behaviour to
younger members'. She also noted that as far as Annie was concerned, 'we all know it is a subject on which she has cause to be
specially sensitive'.

Berridge was a great advocate of the teachings of the odd
visionary, Thomas Lake Harris, whose ideas included the advocacy of 'Karezza' (sexual intercourse with neither movement
nor orgasm) and a somewhat cavalier attitude to monogamy.
Not content with promoting the philosophy of Harris's
'Brotherhood of the New Life' in veiled manner in the pages of

A.E. Waite's journal, *The Unknown World,* and in slightly more open manner in his privately printed pamphlets (under the pseudonym of Respiro), Berridge touted his odd ideas around the Golden Dawn. Coupled with his extremely forward behaviour towards the ladies, he soon found himself opposed by senior members who objected, as Mrs Rand put it, to his 'spreading among the ignorant a perverted indecent aspect of one of the Higher Truths'. The higher truth in question concerned the union of humans and elementals and while many of the adepts objected to Berridge's ideas, only Annie complained directly to Mathers.

In so doing she set in motion the train of events that would eventually lead to Mathers casting her out of the Order. But it was a longer process than appears from Crowley's notes on the matter, which he wrote in the margins of his own copy of Regardie's *My Rosicrucian Adventure:*

> F.E.R. protested against S.R.M.D. for permitting a 'Flying Roll' called 'On Methods of Reproduction on certain planes contiguous to the Astral'. He naturally rebuked her. She answered back, and was expelled. S.R.M.D. was wholly in the right: we all agreed on this. F.E.R. was a frustrated female.

In its outline this is, more or less, what happened, but there was never such a Flying Roll (although Berridge may have written such a paper) and it was manifestly untrue that all were agreed that Mathers was in the right – leaving aside the fact that Crowley did not enter the Order until long after these events had taken place.

Mathers certainly rebuked Annie and at great length. In a letter of 8 January, 1896, he pointed out the error of her ways, adding sanctimoniously that 'it is no pleasure for me to reprove your faults'. He took exception to some of her comments and explained why:

> The phrases in your letter to which I take exception are: 'I could not accept it as for me, and my present companions, the propriety etc..'.. 'the desirability formed in my present

*In this cartoon (c. 1896) Annie Horniman ('Tabbie') submits to the rule of the autocratic Mathers. The artist is unkown.*

state of contemplating such alliances being made by my friends etc. etc.' . . . You have every right to your own opinion regarding yourself, but what your companions do is a matter for their consideration and consciences. And now I will show you how this is an error in occult working, and why. When you entered the Order, you took the motto of 'Fortiter et Recte', that is, you left the 'Miss Horniman' personality outside the Order. Do not forget that the words 'person', 'personality', are derived from the Latin word 'Persona' which means 'a mask.' Now if, in the Order, you will dwell on the outer personalities of the others with whom you are associated; to such an extent that you are actually hindered in working spiritually by their neighbourhood, as you insinuate you would be, it is a sure proof that you have brought far too much of your own personality into the working of 'Fortiter et Recte'. Why, even if you were surrounded by the Qlipoth you ought by this time to be able to protect yourself and continue your operation.

Assuredly, if in an operation of the Light you allow your personality as 'Miss Horniman' to act as a factor, you will awake immediately the Forces of your Evil Persona. Thus, were it the invocation of Adonai, or Spiritual Development, you would have a horrible influx of the exact opposite of the pure, into your sphere; disgusting and obscene thoughts etc. in other words, you would awake the Development of the Evil Persona, through the Human. If, on the contrary, you are not 'Miss Horniman', but an initiate striving after Light, the Evil Persona cannot arise.

Whether these extraordinary comments say more about Mathers' sexual attitudes or those of Annie Horniman is a moot point. That his ideas were unusual is clear from a further comment in the same letter:

I do not want to rake up the matter of your previous letters, but I may say: re Amore [Mrs A.J. Carden] – she was recommended Elemental marriage because of in her case the *extreme* danger of invoking an incubus instead of a Fay, through want of self-control.

This letter evoked a submissive reply, but later letters to Annie were both rude and condescending and eventually she openly rebelled.

In September 1896, Soror Fortiter et Recte resigned from her office as Sub-Praemonstratrix of Isis-Urania. She had no wish to be involved with Mathers' Celtic politics. She had ceased to send money to Mina, and she resented the fact that Mathers was continuing to make unjust charges against her to other members of the Order, mostly behind her back.

Mathers accepted her resignation with an ill grace and sent his bizarre 'Manifesto' to the Second Order Adepts, over whom he felt his authority crumbling. This was followed by an abusive letter to Annie on 22 November, 1896. Although she had accepted the demands made in the 'Manifesto', he demanded from

*In this telegram to Annie Horniman in October 1899, Mathers implied for the first time that Westcott had been less than honest about the foundation of the Order.*

her a further submission to his will in respect of 'the *working of the Order* of the R.R. et A.C., and that of the G.D., as well as in the teaching of both'. Accusing her of '*utterly uncalled for* spite and hostility' and of 'injuring me by *every* means in your power, from endeavouring to undermine my authority in the Order down to reducing me to poverty in the Outer World' he yet told her that 'I have always and shall always value the great amount of useful and unselfish work you did in both Orders'. Having bitten the hand that fed him, he realised that she was still his only source of income. But it was too late. Mina wrote a week later seeking money, but none was forthcoming and Mathers immediately expelled Soror Fortiter et Recte from the Order, telling her that 'As regards your conduct to me and VNR personally, I consider it *abominable*'. He also accused her of 'intense arrogance, narrowness of judgement and self-conceit' – all of which applied equally, if not to a far greater degree, to his own behaviour. Most cruel of all, he reminded her of an earlier episode in Paris:

136

I could not consider that the person whom I saw shuffling her feet and crying in a hysterical attack in the Musee Guimet because the style of Indian Art affected her nerves unpleasantly – and who on recovering from this attack made VNR and myself solemnly promise not only to warn *but to check her in any and every way, no matter how,* if at any future time we thought she was beginning to show any trace of development of hereditary mania – such a person, I say, would be utterly unfit to correct me in the extremely complex administration of such an Order as the Rosicrucian.

Other members saw her in a more favourable light and attempted to have her reinstated, without success, despite 30 members of the Second Order having signed a petition in her favour. Some felt that they ought not to defy Mathers, given his relationship with the Secret Chiefs. One of the members, Allan Bennett, thought that the expulsion was justified: 'On the one occasion when I attended her classes', he wrote to Gardner, who had organised the petition, 'I was beyond all measure shocked at the casual and flippant treatment of the Spirit Vision there set forth.' It was a lone hostile voice, and resentment against Mathers deepened within the Order.

For her part, Annie was fed up with the whole affair. On Christmas Day she wrote to William Peck (the Imperator of Amen-Ra Temple) telling him that she was 'tired of secrecy' and set out 'the exact statement of my insubordination for which I am now expelled. The proofs are in my bank books which Mrs Rand can get at and show you.' She then detailed all the payments made to the Mathers, and told Peck the nature of the letters she had received from Mathers. The final paragraph of the letter put her on the moral high ground:

I have only received the news from Mrs Rand this morning that I have been publicly expelled. I make no defence and I will leave no schism behind me – but I wish that all honest people should be clearly informed as to what my actual crime is.

Annie remained outside the Order for three years, returning only after the Rebellion of 1900 and Mathers' expulsion. She did not, however, abandon her astrological studies and in 1899 was writing to Westcott to tell him that 'I am flattered that my Astrology is so good that Mrs Westcott is incredulous as to my veracity'. And just as her occult practices had been kept in shape, so had her strength of will. Once returned to the Golden Dawn, as 'Scribe for the Second Order', she tussled again with Berridge, instructing her solicitor to deal with him firmly:

Dear Mr Shelton                                    May 10th , '00

The following is a quotation from a letter which I received on May 5th. The writer is Mrs Ross-Scott of 4 Kingswood Road, Upper Norwood. 'One thing I'll tell you before I close; Dr Berridge said to me, that if you helped... and the others with your money to fight..., he would tell your father you were dabbling in magic and he felt sure your father would have you shut up in an Asylum; whether your father would or could do so, you know better than I do, but forewarned is forearmed.'

I know that this is very absurd but I want Dr Berridge made to understand that I can protect myself. My father might try to take legal steps against me on any pretext however unjust. Dr Berridge doubtless thinks that I have further expectations from my father and so imagines that this is an efficacious sort of threat. My real dislike for him came from my objection to the sort of literature he distributed amongst my friends. I have never done him any harm. Could you legally write immediately and tell him in the proper form that he must 'shut up'? I only want to frighten him. He has a terror of publicity, and I have nothing in my life of which I am ashamed. *

With kind regards, Believe me,

Yours sincerely

A.E.F. Horniman

* He must be made to understand that such libellous statements about me must stop. He would look very foolish when asked to explain publicly what 'magic' means.

Nor was Berridge to be her only target. The new Scribe for

the Second Order found that the administration of the Order was in a complete mess and berated Florence Farr, who was responsible for the day to day organisation, over her *laissez faire* attitude. She also objected strongly to the independent groups within the Order, of which the Sphere Group was the most important, and wished to see the now abandoned examination system restored. In this she was supported by Yeats, but the Executive Council opposed her and when the matter was put before a General Meeting Annie was defeated.

But her opposition continued and as the Golden Dawn transformed itself into the M. R. after the Horos trial, so Soror Fortiter et Recte continued to inveigh against the groups. It was all in vain because the new triad of Chiefs – Felkin, Bullock and Brodie-Innes – had no intention of letting her order them around. The groups were, in any case, no longer active. Annie insisted on performing a Banishing Ceremony to ensure that the groups' Symbol (which she considered to be highly dangerous) was dissipated on the astral plane, and presented a long memorandum to the Chiefs to justify her stance. They agreed that she should perform the ritual but when she further insisted that ex-members of the groups should pay a proportion of the rent for No. 36 Blythe Road (where their activities had been carried out), they refused to take any action, perhaps because Annie had cast aspersions on the honesty of both Felkin and Mrs Rand: 'the low idea that "it does not matter" in regard to honesty', as she expressed it. Many of the members had already left the Order and in practical terms there was little that they could have done even if they had accepted this strange demand. To Annie, however, it was a matter of honour. She wished the money to go 'to some public or masonic charity' and added, 'Naturally members in the poverty clause would not need to pay', but above all it was to support her invincible rectitude:

> Because certain members have such a low idea of my personal uprightness, I am the more anxious to let them see that I believe they are capable of behaving uprightly.

The Chiefs declined to give her the opportunity to be so

*Florence Farr, c.1890, after she had separated from her husband, Edward Emery.*

publicly moral, and in February 1903 she left the Golden Dawn for good. For the remainder of her life (she lived until 1937) she devoted herself to the theatre. Whether she considered ritual drama more important than play-acting, or the reverse, is, however, a question that must remain unanswered; what is certain is that both she and the Golden Dawn were enriched by her presence in it.

## Florence Farr

The Sphere Group, which united Yeats and Annie Horniman in their total opposition to it, was the creation of Florence Farr. She was a friend of Miss Horniman and for all her life a close friend of Yeats, however ill-conceived he might consider her magical group to be. All three were united in their dual love of magic and of the theatre, but whereas Yeats took magic into his drama, Florence Farr – like Annie Horniman – brought theatre into the Golden Dawn.

She was born on 7 July, 1860, at Bromley in Kent, the youngest child of William Farr, a medical practitioner who achieved fame as a medical statistician, and became Assistant Registrar-General. He died in 1883, but Florence was already leading an independent life. Having passed through Queen's College, she took up acting as a profession. A year after her father's death she married a young actor, Edward Emery, and for four years endured an unsatisfactory marriage. But although her husband had left for America in 1888, Florence did not divorce him until 1894. In the interim she took up scandalously with Bernard Shaw and more discreetly with the Golden Dawn.

In the Order's Address Book she appears as Mrs Florence Beatrice Emery, of 123 Dalling Road, Ravenscourt Park, London, for until her divorce she was usually known as 'Mrs Emery.' She entered the Order in July 1890 and was admitted to the Inner Order in August 1891, taking the motto 'Sapientia Sapienti Dono Data'. Her advancement was rapid. Within a year she became Sub-Cancellaria and after Dr Woodman's death she was appointed Cancellaria of Isis-Urania. Technically this made her one of the three Chiefs, but Mathers' autocracy was such that only one Chief ruled in practice. In 1893, Westcott resigned as Praemonstrator and Florence took his place, remaining in office until 1900. When Mathers was deposed, she acted as 'Chief Adept in Anglia'. But the reconstructed Order became too rigid and with the return of Annie Horniman all the old bickering about the secret groups began again. Florence wanted none of this and in 1902 she left the Golden Dawn. However she was not, as we shall see, entirely done with magical societies.

Within the Second Order, Florence was responsible for three of the Flying Rolls: a part of No. II, 'Three Suggestions on Will Power'; No. IV, 'Example of Mode of attaining to spirit Vision'; and No. XIII 'A Lecture on Secrecy and Hermetic Love'. The latter is the one Flying Roll known to have been borrowed by Yeats. It was issued to him by Westcott on 22 July, 1893. It is also the most interesting of her official Golden Dawn writings.

After explaining the need for both secrecy and silence – 'In darkness and stillness the Archetypal forms are conceived and the forces of nature germinated' – Florence launched into an exhortation:

> Free yourselves from your environments. Believe nothing without weighing and considering it for yourselves; what is true for one of us, may be utterly false for another. The God who will judge you at the day of reckoning is the God who is within you now; the man or woman who would lead you this way or that, will not be there then to take the responsibility off your shoulders.

> 'The old beauty is no longer beautiful; the new truth is no longer true', is the eternal cry of a developing and really vitalised life. Our civilisation has passed through the First Empire of pagan sensualism; and the Second Empire of mistaken sacrifice, of giving up our own consciousness, our own power of judging, our own independence, our own courage. And the Third Empire is awaiting those of us who can see – that not only in Olympus, not only nailed to the Cross, but in *ourselves is God*. For such of us, the bridge between flesh and spirit is built; for such among us hold the Keys of life and death.

> In this connection, I may mention that the 0=0 of the Grade of Neophyte has a deep significance as a symbol; a 0 means nothing to the world – to the initiate in the form of a circle it means *all*, and the aspiration of the Neophyte should be 'In myself I am nothing, in Thee I am all; Oh bring me to that self, which is in Thee'.

It is very much a reflection of her own free spirit, rebelling against the mores of her time. She was, remarked Shaw, 'in violent reaction against Victorian morals, especially sexual and domestic morals'.

When Mathers made his shattering denouncement of Westcott and the forged Anna Sprengel letters, Florence was badly shaken. She had earlier sought to verify the origins of the cipher manuscript and had written to Westcott to obtain Anna Sprengel's address:

July 28th, '98

My Dear S.A.

I am so sorry to have missed you the other day and thought that perhaps you were going to write to me. I am off on Saturday to Edenbridge Town (The Cottage).

Will you mind writing and telling me the exact address of the little German village we wot of. I may have an opportunity of investigating it soon. Is there anything I can do for you in any way?

Yours always fraternally

S.S.D.D.

Three days later Westcott replied: 'I suppose you refer to Dahme, Prussia, I think near Berlin where was the Lodge "Licht, Liebe, Leben", to which our branch of Rosics. is *alleged* to have been related.'

Vague and qualified though this was, Florence thanked him 'for the information about the Masonic Lodge. I believe some interesting information may be gained from it.' Whatever she intended to do, nothing seems to have come of it, but she retained her faith in the mystical adepts and viewed Mathers rather than Westcott, of whom she remained very fond, as the villain of the piece.

Brodie-Innes, writing to Dr Felkin in 1913, recalled his amazement at Florence's actions in 1900:

Early in 1900 Mrs Emery wrote to me that Mathers was hopelessly involved with Crowley, and Crowley was such an utter blackguard that there was a dead-lock. I replied – more than half in joke – 'the only course seems to be either that Mathers expels you, or you expel Mathers'. To my surprise she took it seriously, and wrote 'that is precisely what *we have done'*. I told her then it was absurd and unconstitutional. That the so-called 'Council of Adepts' had no corporate existence, and no society or club in the world could take such a step. Yeats told the story to George Moore as a joke, and Moore put it into his Reminiscences.

Yeats, of course, was then beginning his battle against the groups and doubtless enjoyed stories told at Florence's expense. But what was her Sphere Group?

The purpose of the group was 'the transmutation of evil into good' by way of a complex process of visualisation involving astral travelling through an expanding sequence of spheres. The method was set out in a long and detailed 'Instruction issued by S.S.D.D. to Members of the Sphere Group. March 1901'. 'We have from the first', wrote Florence,

> been formulated in purely R.R. et A.C. symbolism, and now that we are obliged, to a certain extent, to consider ourselves as a body of students, in relation to other members of that Order, I think it best to define our position more accurately.
>
> We have no connection with any Egyptian Adept. We group ourselves symbolically round the symbol of the axis of the Sphere, taking the instructions given in the Star Maps lecture as the basis of our Operation.
>
> We are to consider the axis of our globe as consisting of the following symbols: The Cup of the Stolistes containing a burning heart. This emblem is to be considered as occupying the central axis and the intermediate spaces of the globe between the axis and the surface.
>
> It will be seen in practice that when the operation of gradual enlargement is being carried out, each Sephiroth widens out like a ray from a central Tiphareth for, in a sense, all operations are commenced from the Sephirotic globe of Tiphareth or the absolute Centre – the centre of the Heart.

She went on to give very precise details of the way in which each globe should be formulated, with exact dimensions and locations. The first stage of the process 'is to retain an ideal ten Sephiroth projected on a sphere in which each Sephira is the size of the aura of an ordinary human being, say 10 feet in diameter – roughly the whole sphere 90 feet in diameter'.

The first sphere was to be 'formed astrally over the Headquarters of the Order', while successive spheres were to be nine miles in diameter, then 2700 miles, 8100 miles and eventually the diameter of the solar system. Finally, the solar system itself is visualised as 'a pale star in the centre of the operation of the sphere'. At this point the visionary imagines rays of light between the Sephiroth and repeats the mantra, 'Oh thou of whom I am a part I am all of thee'. Having reached this maximum expansion the group now draws slowly in, at each stage repeating the phrase 'Let Ra live, let Apophis be destroyed', and beating down the Qlipoth. The instruction concludes with a list of the sephirotic and elemental role of each of the 12 participants.

Given its basis in Order symbolism and its clear altruism, it is difficult to see just why Annie Horniman objected so strongly to the Sphere Group.

Florence was not confined to astral travelling outside the regular Order ceremonies. She was interested also in alchemy, astrology, the kabbalah, and – above all – Egyptology, writing on most of these topics for Westcott's *Collectanea Hermetica* series of occult handbooks. Later she wrote a brief study of the Hebrew alphabet – *The Way of Wisdom* (1900) – and produced a remarkable series of articles on her esoteric interests for *The Occult Review*. In one of these 'The Rosicrucians and Alchemists', her attitude to life is spelled out as well as her ideas on occultism:

Now the Rose of the Rosicrucians was a more complicated symbol than the Cup. As we have seen the cup was a symbol of creation, and its form was connected with the symbol of a circle in contrast to the Cross. The symbol of the Rose contains five petals and five divisions of the calyx. It is evidently the symbol of creation in activity not in potentiality only. Perhaps we may believe the Rose to be a symbol of the subtle body of man which is one with nature, and the Cross the symbol of the body and the name or word of man. The Union of the Rose and Cross would symbolise a man able to unite himself with the great powers of Nature, or tatwas, familiar to us under their Hindoo names Akasa, Vayu, Tejas, Apas and Prithivi, or the kingdoms of sound, sensation, perception, absorption and reproduction, more commonly called hearing, touching, seeing, eating and generating.

Now the notion of obtaining the natural powers of an adept

is most apparent in the traditions that come through Egypt and Chaldea, and the idea of the super-essential state in contrast to power is most apparent in the Oriental traditions. The high caste Oriental has the aristocratic spirit that conceives the height of life on this world to consist in delicacy of perception associated with perfect self-satisfaction, while the democratic spirit of the West cannot conceive itself without desires, struggles and potencies for gratifying desires; democracy wishes to do and to have; aristocracy is sufficient unto itself.

This elevation of the Eastern spirit (which was very much a subjective, personal interpretation) followed her joining the Theosophical Society in 1902 and was part of an oriental drift that would ultimately take her to a teaching career in Ceylon.

And yet, Egypt remained her obsession. Seeing in them an Egyptian origin, Florence was also fascinated with Tarot cards which she interpreted after her own manner, as Brodie-Innes recalled in his article on the Tarot Cards, written for *The Occult Review* in 1919:

> I was interested to find that what [Mrs Lee] told me of the Tarot was well known to another friend of mine, the late Mrs Florence Farr Emery, who herself claimed Romani descent, and had a great store of strange learning. She it was who first pointed out to me the correspondence of the interpretations of the pip cards with the Pythagorean system, greatly to my delight, for the meanings usually ascribed to the cards had seemed merely empirical, and founded on no system, as indeed are the meanings ascribed to cards by the ordinary type of fortune-teller today. More doubtful were Mrs Emery's suggestions of Egyptian correspondences. She was a diligent student of Egyptology, though perhaps not quite as much of an authority as her friends claimed, and with natural enthusiasm was apt to see ancient Egypt everywhere.

This judgement was supported by A.E. Waite, who was not noted for agreeing with any statement made by Brodie-Innes.

In April 1901, Waite attended a lecture on Ancient Egypt given by Florence Farr (as Soror Sapientia) but he was not especially impressed by her speaking:

> I understand that she is thinking of taking to public
> speaking, but I do not think that she will ever be a good
> speaker, in spite of the wonderful charm of her voice and the
> strange effect of her large and clear green eyes. She is
> desultory, scrappy, abounds in unmeaning catch phrases
> intended to connect the points of her discourse but not
> doing so, and she leaves the majority of her sentences
> unfinished.

About her competence in Egyptology he was ambiguous:

> She knows, however, a good deal of her subject – or so she
> impresses me – and hence it follows that (1) that it is not
> necessary, or perhaps even desirable, to go to Egypt in order
> to be learned in things Egyptian; and (2) that you can know
> much of antiquity without being able to construe its dead
> languages.

Waite, of course, took Marcus Worsley Blackden as his guide, and he was a real Egyptologist who had spent several seasons with the Egyptian Exploration Fund.

Two years later, however, Waite was initiated into Florence's 'nameless rite' which he refers to only as the SOS while making it clear that its symbolism, ethos and essence were all Egyptian. He says very little about it, implying only that it was quite distinct from any other rite that he knew. When he entered the SOS on 22 March, 1903, he noted in his diary only that, 'It was an experience altogether strange and sudden and it took place as most ceremonies will in an obscure street, where faded respectability struggles unsuccessfully enough with bad drains and a thriving trade in harlotry'.

The ceremony of initiation was completed on 18 April, but respecting his obligation, Waite recorded nothing at all of its working.

As Florence may be presumed to have produced the ritual, it may also be presumed to have had the flavour of her Egyptian plays and to have included speeches such as this from *The Shrine of the Golden Hawk:*

In my dreams I went into the forest where the bronze and gold serpents coil like flames amid the leaves, and they made me wise with great sayings, and the spirits of power passed into my spirit; for the forest was the forest of knowledge. But when I held the image of the Hawk exalted on the standard of the crossed pole before the serpents, they paled and grew dim in the presence of a strength greater than theirs; and as I looked the wood became silent and empty, and the creatures of the wisdom, which is of time, faded away.

People too, fade away, and Florence was all too conscious of flying time. Yeats referred to her last years in his dedication to *A Vision:*

Florence Farr coming to her fiftieth year, dreading old age and fading beauty, had made a decision we all dreamt of at one time or another, and accepted a position as English teacher in a native school in Ceylon that she might study Oriental thought, and had died there.

In 1912 Florence sailed for Ceylon to take up her post at the Ramanathan College at Induvil on the Jaffna peninsula, and for five years she gave out English and took in Hinduism until her death from cancer in 1917.

Mina Mathers had been unable to escape from the Golden Dawn, but Florence Farr – like Annie Horniman – had given to it, taken from it, and passed on.

# CHAPTER SIX

# Mystics and Magicians: Lives of the Lesser Adepts

All the women who rose to prominence in the Golden Dawn were strong-willed, single-minded and in rebellion against the social constraints placed upon their sex by Victorian society. No common set of characteristics can be found, however, among the men of the Order. It is almost impossible to assemble a representative group of typical 'men of the Order'. Their only common conviction was that the Hermetic Order of the Golden Dawn would, in some undefined manner, bring them spiritual enlightenment and thereby the recognition that eluded them in the world outside. There was no common social or vocational background. Many of them were small businessmen and from the professions. A sizeable minority were actual or would-be writers and artists. A selection of odd fish drawn from these groups is presented in this chapter. The eccentrics were, as in most social groups of the time, the writers and artists.

## The Revd. W.A. Ayton (1816-1908)

Lawyers and medical doctors were plentiful in the Order, but there were only two clergymen – in its early days anyway. One of these, the Revd. T.W. Lemon, advanced no further than the Neophyte Grade and soon departed. The other rose to prominence and eventually presided over the Order as one of its triad of Chiefs. He also had the distinction of being the oldest member of the Golden Dawn,

The Revd. William Alexander Ayton did not enter the Golden Dawn alone. He was admitted as Frater Virtute Orta

*The Revd. William Alexander Ayton (1816–1908) used his motto 'Virtute Orta Occidunt Rarius' on his 'Receipt and Undertaking', which he signed on 25 April, 1892.*

Occidunt Rarius ('Those that rise by virtue rarely fall') in July 1888 accompanied by his wife Anne, Soror Quam Potero Adjutabo ('I will help as much as I can'). Ten months later he wrote to F.L. Gardner about their experiences in the Order:

> Ladies are admitted. Mrs Ayton and I went through an examination this last time in London, Mrs A. passing without making one mistake. Upon request an MS is sent to you to copy, in which subject you have to be examined. Mrs A. learned the Hebrew letters so as to write them within the last year. We are well satisfied with it.

Ayton's satisfaction with his wife's meagre achievement contrasts with his own knowledge of occultism which was more extensive than that of almost all of his fellow members – the result of a lifetime's quest. Ayton was born at Bloomsbury in central London on 28 April 1816. His studies began as a child – or so it would seem from an address that he gave to the members of Horus Temple at Bradford in 1890:

> Even as a boy, I had a strong perception of the occult. In

*Aleister Crowley's list of prominent members of the Order, written in the margins of his copy of Regardie's* My Rosicrucian Adventure *(1936).*

*Allan Bennett, most-famous of all*

penalties attached to the most awe-inspiring obligations in order to ensure that secrecy. So well have these obligations with but one or two exceptions been kept that the general public knows next to nothing about the Order, its teaching, or the extent and nature of its membership. Though this book will touch upon the teaching of the Golden Dawn, concerning its membership as a whole the writer will have nothing to say, except perhaps to repeat what may already be more or less well-known. For instance, it is common knowledge that W. B. Yeats, Arthur Machen and, if rumour may be trusted, the late Arnold Bennett were at one time among its members, together with a good many other writers and artists.

With regard to the names given in Dr. Westcott's statement it is necessary that we bestow to them some little attention in order to unravel, so far as may be possible, the almost inextricable confusion which has characterised every previous effort to detail the history of the Order. M.E.V. was the motto chosen by Dr. William Robert Woodman, an eminent Freemason of the last century. Sapere Aude and Non Omnis Moriar were the two mottos used by Dr. Westcott, an antiquarian, scholar, and coroner by profession. S.R.M.D. or S. Rhiogail Ma Dhream was the motto of S.L. MacGregor Mathers, the translator of *The Greater Key of King Solomon*, the *Book of the Sacred Magic of Abramelin the Mage*, and *The Qabalah Unveiled*, which latter consisted of certain portions of the Zohar prefixed by an introduction of high erudition. He also employed the Latin motto Deo Duce Comite Ferro. S. D. A. was the abbreviation of the motto Sapiens Dominabitur Astris chosen by a Fräulein Anna Sprengel of Nüremberg, Germany. Such were the actors on this occult stage, this the *dramatis personae* in the background of the commencement of the Order. More than any other figures who may later have prominently figured in its government and work, these are the four

*Blackden painter. + Gerald Kelly R.A. A.E. Waite*

*Dr Berridge : fashionable homeopath*
*Mrs Oscar Wilde. Sir H. + Lady Colvile . Serge*
*[Governor of Gibraltar]*
*Cecil Jones . Mrs Simpson - errant singer*
*Lucile Hill - Prima Donna . Ely Star - astrologer*
*Brodie-Innes : very fine novelist. Chas. Rosher*

reading the classical writers at school, I perceived constant allusion to something mysterious, which greatly excited my curiosity, where other boys saw nothing at all. I only got laughed at for talking about it and consequently I became very reticent but only thought the more. In those days the difficulties in gaining information on this all-important subject were very great.

'You who live in these days,' he added, 'may consider yourselves very fortunate indeed.'

He later became absorbed in alchemy after reading the works of Thomas Vaughan at the British Museum. Parish duties however proved so demanding that further occult research was curtailed for some years. Once he was established as Vicar of

Chacombe in Oxfordshire, he 'began upon Cornelius Agrippa' and studied Emanuel Swedenborg until:

> I perceived that marvellous as were his abilities and universal knowledge and genius, he was only another added to the long roll of Hermetic Philosophers who have gone wrong, and that he is not really a reliable teacher.

From Swedenborg, he turned to Paracelsus, although with little success:

> After wading thro' his works and putting them in practice so far as making Talismans with the utmost care, precisely according to his directions and, after all, finding them inert, or nearly so, I perceived that I was knocking my head against a stone wall in attempting to put them in practice without a something further which something I could not then grasp.

Ayton finally concluded that 'all the writers I have mentioned never intended their writings to be understood by the uninitiated'. In order to make progress in his occult studies Ayton realised that he would have to be initiated which 'was not permitted without the obligation of secrecy under the severest penalties'.

Having determined to become initiated, Ayton next read 'with the greatest avidity' the works of Eliphas Lévi, 'almost as soon as they were published'. He went on to meet 'an intimate friend of Eliphas Lévi', Dr Desjardin, from whom he received 'what he called an initiation' which he found unsatisfactory. Desjardin furthermore expected payment for his 'initiations'.

Ayton progressed to Maurice Vidal Portman and the Order of Light. Portman, he recalled,

> told me a very curious circumstance, which I have never been able to bring myself thoroughly to believe. He said he had not only seen, but also had been initiated by Count St. Germain then not long since. Now, seeing that the Count could not have been less than 90 when he left Paris about the end of the last century, this would make him to be somewhere about 180 years old. I asked him how old he

looked, and he said 40, and added that the Adepts who lived long always contrived to look about 40 years. My friend Portman may or may not have been deceived in some way. However, I learned good deal of Oriental Occultism from him. He had rented a house on purpose in London, and fitted up a room with all the paraphernalia of an Occult Lodge, and there he gave Initiations in regular form according to what he had seen in India. I was initiated.

In 1878 Ayton was also initiated into Freemasonry and soon afterwards joined the infant Theosophical Society. He also met T.H. Pattinson.

From what I then saw of the strong proclivities of Yorkshiremen for Occultism, I had the greatest desire to organise a Lodge somewhere in this neighbourhood [in Bradford] for carrying on the study of it.

Ultimately, the Horus Temple was the result. Ayton also looked upon occultism as part of a spiritual mission:

Herein is the use of the Occult Sciences, that the knowledge of them tends to rescue the human race from this degradation and final extinction . . . A few Adepts can exert their influence upon the ignorant masses, form a stable government with wise laws, administered with justice and equity, and a certain amount of happiness be restored to mankind. Then, at last, can commerce, wealth and, at last, luxury, flourish. It is only the self-denying, disinterested and benevolent Adept who can effect all this.

Ayton was a fervent believer in elemental beings, practical magic and the efficacy of alchemy. He was also the natural prey of every occult confidence trickster. In 1886 he had been highly embarrassed by appearing as a director on the prospectus of The Hermetic Colony Association Ltd. It was a bogus company set up to milk the public of some £20,000 by selling shares in an absurd enterprise that sought to promote a strictly vegetarian community in the State of Georgia which was purported to be living off the proceeds of a putative gold mine. Ayton was not the only dupe. Two other future members of the Golden Dawn were also innocently involved.

With this swindle behind him and secure within the confines of the Golden Dawn, Ayton concentrated on practical occultism. By 1892 he felt confident in advising Gardner how to go about expelling an unwanted elemental:

> The Pentagram used with the proper invocations &c &c, according to the rules of the Quabalah, is potent to expel these creatures. They say also that the burning of fir cones drives them away, but I have never tried it. Read about the Pentagram and Hexagram in Eliphas Lévi. Do you know any Jew Qabalist who would do it for you?

He was well aware of the problems such elementals could bring in their wake. This is clearly demonstrated in an earlier letter to Gardner:

> I have lately had a strange reminder in a mysterious way, that I am treading very close upon the regions of the Gnomes, and that if I reveal too much, there exists a power which can inflict sudden death. As I have only sought the elixir of Life, this is the more strange, but it behoves me to be careful.

Ayton's caution was often interpreted by others as a pathological anxiety. W.B. Yeats, who described him as 'an old white-haired Oxfordshire clergyman, the most panic-stricken person I have ever known', recalled the old man's fear of spirits: '[Ayton] took me aside that he might say – "I hope you never invoke spirits – that is a very dangerous thing to do. I am told that even the planetary spirits turn upon us in the end." I said, "Have you ever seen an apparition?" "Oh yes, once," he said,

> "I have my alchemical laboratory in a cellar under my house where the Bishop cannot see it. One day, I was walking up and down there, when I heard another footstep walking up and down beside me. I turned and saw a girl I had been in love with when I was a young man, but she died long ago. She wanted me to kiss her. Oh no, I would not do that." "Why not?", I said, "Oh she might have got power over me."'

Ayton also told Yeats of his alchemical experiments:

> 'Has your alchemical research had any success?' I said, 'Yes,
> I once made the elixir of Life. A French alchemist said it had
> the right smell and the right colour' [the alchemist may have
> been Eliphas Lévi, who visited England in the 'sixties, and
> would have said anything], 'but the first effect of the elixir is
> that your nails fall out and your hair falls off. I was afraid that
> I might have made a mistake and that nothing else might
> happen, so I put it away on a shelf. I meant to drink it when
> I was an old man, but when I got it down the other day, it
> had all dried up.'
>
> (*Autobiographies*, p.228)

Yeats may have been cynical, but Mathers saw Ayton as one who 'unites us to the great adepts of antiquity' and respected his learning to such an extent that when the time came for Ayton to enter the Second Order, 'I underwent the first Exams and was ready and willing and capable of undergoing all further Exams, but Mathers said, as I knew so much it was not necessary for me to go through the formality of Exams, and I was admitted to 5 = 6 [Westcott] officiating'.

Perhaps Mathers looked on Ayton with affection, for, as Ayton told Gardner in a letter of June 1890, it was he who had married the Mathers:

> We have been busy with having Miss Bergson here for the
> time required by Law for Publication of Banns of Marriage,
> which ended in Mr MacGregor Mathers coming down last
> Monday, marrying her in my Church and carrying her off.

Subsequently Mina Mathers painted Ayton's portrait in oils, which, many years later, he showed to A.E. Waite. Waite, however, was not impressed. 'It is certainly very bad', he noted in his diary (20 April, 1903), 'but is supposed to indicate a certain capacity and it is possible that she might have improved'. How just or unjust was this comment we cannot tell, for the portrait has disappeared. By 1903 the old Golden Dawn had broken

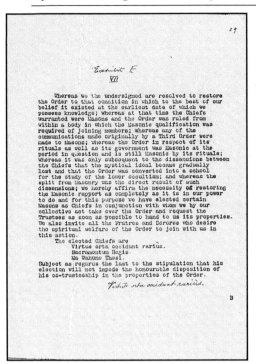

*Ayton's copy of the resolution to found the Independent and Rectified Rite of the Golden Dawn (1903).*

with the Mathers' and both Ayton and Waite held somewhat jaundiced opinions of the couple.

It is also probable that Ayton's disillusionment with Mathers began long before the schism of 1900, for he seems to have become convinced that Mathers was both 'a victim and an emissary' of the Jesuits, or 'Black Brothers', as he preferred to call them. 'Papal aggression' had long been one of Ayton's most enduring terrors, but his growing obsession with the Jesuits irritated even Waite, who was generally tolerant of the old man's phobias: 'Of the Jesuits generally I heard more than enough', he noted in his diary after a visit to Ayton in 1903, 'things ridiculous beyond bearing'. Such things included Ayton's conviction that Yeats was an agent of the 'Black Brothers', as had apparently been Eliphas Lévi and both Gladstone and Disraeli!

We should not, then, be surprised to find Mathers creeping into the astral travels of Ayton and his wife – or rather into their 'spirit visions', attainment of which was a part of Second Order practices, and with which both the Aytons were familiar as both had been admitted into the grade of Adeptus Minor in 1889. In his record of 'spirit visions' for December 1891, Ayton recorded the following:

> Dec 9th Anne, [saw] female figure seated at a long dark desk on N. side of a long narrow corridor, large windows to N. but did not give much light. Behind her stood a man stooping over her – very much in the gloom. He was Mathers. Farther E., in a little better light, another man – he had his back turned to bright light in E. In far E. much brighter light which I was aiming to get at.

> Dec 10th Anne – same at first as yesterday – in S.W. corner crept in Blackwell [Anna Blackwell, a fellow member of the Order], looked very strange and out of place – crept slowly up till she passed S'Rioghail [Mathers], who turned and looked at her. No. of bright figures in E. Blackwell went towards them, but did not get far. Female figure at desk seemed to escape S'Rioghail and go towards light.

In the real world the Aytons escaped from Mathers in 1900, siding with the other adepts of Isis-Urania and expelling him. And it was Ayton who asked Westcott to join them, albeit to meet with a rebuff. Westcott promised to lend Ayton the original cipher manuscripts (he never did) but declined to take part in the struggle for the Order: 'It seems to me', he wrote, 'your friends must remain under Mr M. or resign – I will not lead nor join a schism'. Ayton, however, was made of sterner stuff. Three years later, when the Order split again, he joined Waite and Marcus Worsley Blackden as one of a triad of Chiefs of the Independent and Rectified Rite of the Golden Dawn, and there he remained until his death in 1908. For Waite, as for Mathers, the Revd. William Alexander Ayton had provided continuity, and had united the Golden Dawn with the great adepts of its past.

Ayton's last act in this world was to translate Thomas Smith's *Life of John Dee* and to fill his preface to the book with cautionary words. 'This development of Man's Higher Powers is not without great dangers', he wrote. 'It cuts both ways. A man by its means may become either a God or an Incarnation of evil.'

Dr Dee, he thought, 'was an eminent and melancholy example' of these 'great dangers'. Evidently he had come to see Enochian magic as an evil: still in the Golden Dawn at the time of his death, Ayton was most certainly no longer of it.


# Dr Berridge

Unlike Ayton, the medical men who swarmed in the Golden Dawn were not prone to anxiety. Westcott might be cautious – but it was a caution born of shrewdness, not of timidity. While Dr Felkin and the eccentric Henry Pullen-Burry were both quite content to relate their amazing astral travels to a bemused Conan Doyle, who wisely stayed out of the Order, others were happy to promote lost causes. Dr Robert Theobald propounded Baconian theories, while Charles Lloyd Tuckey advocated hypnosis as a sovereign remedy for psychic illness. Dr Berridge was an exponent of the bizarre philosophy of Thomas Lake Harris. Brash, noisy and utterly impossible, he was one of the few who would remain constantly loyal to Mathers.

Edward William Berridge graduated from London University in 1867 with the degrees of Bachelor of Medicine and Master of Surgery, and almost immediately took up homeopathic medicine. His handbook, the *Complete Repertory to the Homoeopathic Materia Medica,* appeared in 1869. He remained in practice in the Bayswater district of London until 1920. His earliest esoteric involvement was with Thomas Lake Harris and his Brotherhood of the New Life, a cause that Berridge espoused with vigour. He published a constant stream of articles, books and pamphlets extolling the wonders and virtues of Harris's 'work and teaching', a bizarre quasi-Christian philosophy based on spirit revelations and private inspirations, coupled with the promotion of Utopian settlements and of decidedly odd sexual practices. When writing on the Brotherhood of the New Life, Berridge used the pseudonym Respiro, while his motto in the Golden Dawn – singularly apt in view of his irrepressible nature – was 'Resurgam' (I will arise).

Berridge was an early member of Isis-Urania Temple, entering the Neophyte Grade in May 1889. He signed the Pledge Form on 10 May, reversing his decision of the previous year to reject the Order. He advanced rapidly, passed through the Outer Order offices, and in February 1891 entered the Second Order – albeit with less humility than the Chiefs would have liked. His written application had the tone of an equal rather than of a subordinate:

> Dear Mathers,
>
> I am satisfied with the teaching of the G.D. Hermetic Society, and ask as a favour to join the 2nd Order.
>
> I think next Wednesday will suit me, but I cannot be with you till 4 p.m. as my professional engagements keep me here till 3 p.m.
>
> Yrs truly,
>
> E.W. Berridge
>
> I do not know the address of the place of meeting, so please tell me & the nearest way thereto.

For all his lack of deference, Dr Berridge had, within a year of becoming an Adeptus Minor, been appointed Sub-Imperator, and for four years he acted as deputy to the absent Mathers. But in Isis-Urania, effective power still rested with Westcott. After his contretemps with Annie Horniman, and attempted misbehaviour with Mrs Rand, Berridge was demoted.

He had been a valuable teacher of occult wisdom, providing three of the Flying Rolls, but Westcott had become unhappy with Berridge's propagation of dubious and unofficial teachings on sex, and more so with his attempts at their practical application upon the persons of the Order's lady members. Matters were made worse by Berridge's gloating over Annie Horniman's fall from grace.

In 1897 he published one of his many pamphlets on Harris, *The Man, the Seer, the Avatar, or T.L. Harris, the Inspired Messenger of the Cycle,* which included a footnote claiming that a fiendish attempt was made by an occultist to injure me occultly, socially and professionally on account of my advocacy of the New Life. I invoked the aid of the arch-natural powers, and was informed that within 12 months the guilty would be punished. After a series of troubles from an occult source had fallen upon the enemy, and even upon those who had allowed themselves to be drawn into the vortex, just within the predicted time the avenging force of the reverse current culminated and the enemy was occultly crushed; this being followed in a few weeks by a great disaster on the material plane. *Verbum sap.*

Anyone knowing the author to be Berridge could guess that the 'occultist' of this footnote was Annie Horniman, but just in case it should not be absolutely clear, he added a doggerel verse to the copy he sent to H.C. Morris, a fellow-member of Isis-Urania:

Oh! F.E.R. you should not let

Your angry passions rise.

Your feline claws were never meant

To scratch a Frater's eyes.

Morris promptly complained to Gardner, who immediately wrote to Berridge threatening legal action on Miss Horniman's behalf. To this Berridge replied in an evasive manner, arguing that there was no proof that he was the author of the pamphlet. But his wriggling was in vain, for Morris had also sent a copy of the pamphlet to Mathers who left Berridge in no doubt that, favoured adept or not, he would not tolerate this 'triumphant jeering':

I have received from V.H. Fra. 'Cavendo Tutus' [H.C. Morris] a copy of your pamphlet, v. 'The Man, The Seer, Etc.' – on page 11 is a printed note to the latter part of which I take serious exception, & it is aggravated by your having yourself marked the same, & pointed by the addition of a jeering verse against F.E.R. in your handwriting. The whole spirit of it is opposed to the sentiments inculcated in our Second

Order Teaching; & naturally I cannot allow this to pass unnoticed, your conduct herein being a most pernicious example to younger members of the Order. Charity & forbearance, should alike have sealed your lips. It was a regretful necessity to remove Fortiter's name from the roll of the Order; but this does in no sense warrant triumphant jeering over her in disgrace.

I have no choice therefore but to suspend you from the First & Second Orders for a period of 3 months which will expire on the 13th August, & I trust sincerely that you will not err again.

From what I have previously known of you, I should not have expected you to rejoice over the fall of a Frater or Soror. (Letter of 13 May, 1897)

Nor did Berridge err again. He had always supported Mathers' position. It would be he who supported Mathers in the columns of *Light* after the Horos trial. As a true believer in magic he accepted both the reality and the power of Mathers' Secret Chiefs. His views on the Magical Will are set out in 'Some Thoughts on the Imagination', the instructions he wrote as Flying Roll No. V:

When a man imagines he actually creates a form on the Astral or even on some higher plane; and this form is as real and objective to intelligent beings on that plane, as our earthly surroundings are to us.

This form which Imagination creates may have only a transient existence, productive of no important results; or it may be vitalised and then used for good or evil.

To practise magic, both the Imagination and the Will must be called into action, they are co-equal in the work. Nay more, the Imagination must precede the Will in order to produce the greatest possible effect.

The Will unaided can send forth a current, and that current cannot be wholly inoperative; yet its effect is vague and indefinite, because the Will unaided sends forth nothing but the current or force.

The Imagination unaided can create an image and this image

must have an existence of varying duration; yet it can do nothing of importance, unless vitalised and directed by the Will.

When, however, the two are conjoined – when the Imagination creates an image – and the Will directs and uses that image, marvellous magical effects may be obtained.

And not all for the good. The same attitude towards magic appears in more bombastic form in one of Berridge's contributions to A.E. Waite's journal, *The Unknown World*. In 'The Rosicrucian Mystery from the standpoint of a Rosicrucian', 'Resurgam, Fra. R.R. et A.C.' argued that the keys of the forces of nature can be learnt only from the higher Chiefs of the Order, 'and only by those who have first been found worthy of admission, have afterwards passed satisfactorily through the period of their probation, and have finally proved themselves able to use those keys by the development of that occult-power without which mere book-learning is useless'.

Berridge went on to answer the question, 'how is it that the secrets have not been revealed, either by accident, or by treachery'. Accidental exposure, he argued was rare indeed, and 'Doubtless the Higher Chiefs take means for removing any important MSS from those whom they see about to become incapacitated either by illness or death'. And 'as for treachery,' he warned,

> it is not likely that any very important secrets would be given to a member until his fidelity was thoroughly assured and every initiate of an Occult Order knows that his wilful perjury would be followed by unpleasant consequences – *possibly a Coroner's inquest, and a verdict of 'Death from Syncope'.*

Possessed of such views he might have been expected to hurl 'Deadly and Hostile currents of Will' at the 'rebels' of 1900, but he contented himself with helping Mathers to set up the Isis Temple of the Alpha et Omega, and acting as its Cancellarius. The Temple did not always function smoothly. In March 1904, one of the members of Isis, a Mrs Cunningham, brought an action against Berridge to recover the sum of £1,000 which she claimed he owed her for a brooch that she had sold him.

It was a farcical case. Berridge was alleged to have signed a promissory note for £1,000, but when Simon Witte, a friend of Mrs Cunningham and also a member of Isis, turned up at Berridge's home demanding payment, Berridge refused, tearing off his signature from the note, burning it and then calling a policeman to have Witte thrown out.

When the case came to court, Berridge recounted his version of the affair which was reported in the *Daily Telegraph*. Mrs Cunningham had told him that the brooch

> which up to that time he had never seen, had been given by Cagliostro to Marie Antoinette, and put it into his hand. He saw that there was no Royal Crest or initial on it. It was not antique, though it bore the signs of the zodiac. He made some casual remarks about it, and she said, 'It's yours.' It was of neither use nor value to him, but he put it in his pocket. Nothing was said about purchase nor of a promissory note. He had never signed a promissory note in his life, and he did not think he had even seen one. If he were to offer £1,000 for a brooch such as this, he should consider himself a fit candidate for a lunatic asylum.

The signature on the note was, he claimed, a forgery which he had destroyed to protect himself. He was then asked about his activities in the Hermetic Society:

> It has been said that you pretended you could foretell the future, and were gifted with magical powers? If I were gifted with magical powers I would have sent a current through these people and not had this case in court.

He denied that he had claimed to possess magic powers and hastened to assure the court that he was 'simply joking' over the sending of 'a current of strong will power', although he admitted that 'I have concentrated my will power to a certain extent, but I do not call that magic'. He also admitted to a belief in astrology, saying that 'It seems that certain things which have been predicted have come to pass, but it has been mixed up with so much rubbish that it is overwhelmed by it. I am simply an investigator.'

As for this brooch, it was, according to a jeweller who was brought in as an expert witness, worth 'about half-a-crown'. It had been mended very badly, and its age was '25 years at most, and it may be of much later date'. Much the same might have been said about the Order itself.

The judge, Mr Justice Channell, was evidently bemused by the whole affair and in his summing up said that 'it was a curious story. Neither of the parties was quite a normal person from any point of view. Each was a member of this somewhat peculiar society, the objects and nature of which had not been very clearly put before the court.'

He concluded by commenting somewhat ambiguously on the characters of both Mrs Cunningham and Dr Berridge. He summed up by stating that

> The impression left on his mind was that there was something more behind the story than had been gone into. He could not say where the truth lay. The whole thing was left in such a state of doubt that he could not accept the story of the plaintiff as sufficiently reliable to act upon. It might be the fact that these people were of an abnormal character with these beliefs in things that were not generally held accounted for the matters which, to his mind, were unintelligible.

But, 'the burden of proof being on the plaintiff, judgement would be for the defendant'. Thus Berridge escaped, but Mrs Cunningham and her brooch were not to be the last of his scrapes.

His temple continued for another ten years or more, but by 1912, peculiar innovations had made the members restive. Two in particular, Mrs De Bathe and Henry Brasche, were incensed by a demand from Mathers (via Berridge) for a fee of five guineas for conferring on them the 6 = 5 grade of Adeptus Major by letter, no adept grades having been worked ceremonially by Berridge since 1910. They also objected, as Christians of sorts, to Mathers' new ritual for the consecration of a temple, which involved bowing before a statue of Isis, and resigned in protest from Berridge's temple. While still in a fine rage, Brasche visited A.E. Waite and poured out his woes, but it was not the demands for money that had most upset him. 'My informant,' noted Waite in his record of the meeting,

> **was full of the iniquities of Resurgam and told a strange story concerning a Nurse Graham, brought in, I think, by Soror Mystica, whom he visited continually. He boasts of his astral intercourse with a counterpart or affinity in the astral world, by whom he has had three spirit children.**

Presumably a case of the spirit being willing and the flesh weak, but his spirit children may have brought comfort to Berridge in his final years, and they would certainly have proved less of a burden on an old man's pocket than would children of this world.

# Arthur Machen (1863–1947) and A.E. Waite (1857–1942)

As far as the Golden Dawn is concerned, Machen and Waite cannot be separated. They had much in common. Both were born writers who had a lonely and introverted childhood. Each of them came to the Golden Dawn in a search of spiritual identity. Waite came at the end of a journey that had taken him from Roman Catholicism through virtual agnosticism to spiritualism and theosophy. Machen came suddenly and dramatically in the depths of his despair after his wife's death. Both Waite and Machen however came to reject magic as part of the Golden Dawn.

They met in 1886 when Waite was 25 years old and Machen six years his junior. Finding a close natural affinity, they became the best of friends. They argued fiercely over occultism and pursued their literary careers together. Waite was the first to join the Order. He was urged to join by Dr Berridge, and

*Arthur Edward Waite (1857–1942) as he appeared in the early 1900s – the time at which he came to prominence in the Golden Dawn.*

In the end I agreed to join, with the not unexpected and not regrettable result of being refused promptly. The denial was taken by Berridge in no dejected spirit: my application must be repeated a second time, after a certain space. I was to learn later on that those of whom nothing was known were admitted readily, others with preliminary rejections which were cancelled afterwards.

(*Shadows of Life and Thought*, p.125).

His reception into the Neophyte grade took place in January 1891 at Stent Lodge, Dulwich, where Mathers was then living. Waite was not quite sure what to expect, but clearly did not take the matter seriously. He told his wife, 'in appropriately sardonic terms', that

I was engaged on a dark errand, of which nothing could be

declared or hinted, so if I failed to return she must communicate with Scotland Yard and offer certain leading lights on place and time.

But all was well:

> I met, however, with nothing worse than a confounding medley of Symbols, and was handed a brief tabulation of elementary points drawn at haphazard from familiar occult sources: on these I was supposed to answer given questions, did I wish to proceed further. They were subjects about which it turned out that the G D had nothing to communicate that was other than public knowledge.

Nonetheless, he persisted (as would Aleister Crowley who felt the same initial sense of disappointment): 'My dues were paid, my status thus secured, my membership straggled on; and I took some further steps with a vague idea of seeing the business through'. By April 1892, he had advanced to the $4 = 7$ Grade of Philosophus. And then,

> I began to hear things which, in my several positions at the moment, told me that I should be well out of the whole concern. It was not on the score of morality, seeing that there were *Fratres et Sorores*; for on this ground it is just to say that no breath of sandal ever arose in the G D during all that period. It was a question of things which had an equivocal legal aspect and in which leading members of the Order should not have been concerned, had I been informed accurately, as there seems no doubt that I was. I retired or rather demitted without explanation; and if I thanked my stars that in so doing I missed but little, it is more than probable that the Hermetic Order of the G D missed even less. I had no grist in my granaries for a mill of that kind.

What this supposed chicanery was remains unclear, and his fellow-members thought that poverty rather than probity had caused him to leave. In 1893 Waite left the Order, albeit with the door of return left open, for his entry in the Address Book is

*Arthur Machen
(1863–1947), novelist,
actor, man of letters and
mystic, c.1900.*

marked 'in abeyance'. For the next three years his occult activities were confined to lecturing and writing on mysticism, publishing a long series of alchemical translations, and editing *The Unknown World,* all the while watching the Order through the eyes of Dr Berridge.

Finally, Waite decided to return, and in February 1896 he was 'readmitted by ballot', or as he himself preferred to put it, 'I returned to the dubious fold by the unanimous vote of the Fellowship'. But it was not until March 1899 that he entered the Second Order and began, slowly at first, to work towards its commanding heights.

While all this was going on Machen was busy writing and enjoying married life. His early fiction, with its occult themes and overtones of a powerful secret society, appealed to members of the Golden Dawn and both *The Great God Pan* and *The Three Imposters* found their way into the Order library. Their author, however, remained firmly outside the Golden Dawn and had no truck with the magical practices that he knew so well in theory from his years with George Redway, the occult publisher, until the autumn of 1899 when, in a dreadful despair over his wife's death that summer, 'a horror of soul' descended upon him and he felt driven to magic as a way of escape from his torment. Where his 'process' (seemingly some magical form of auto-hypnosis) would have led him cannot be guessed, but Waite saw the danger facing his friend and drew him away from his dark ecstasy into the disciplined occultism of the Golden Dawn.

On 21 November, 1899, Frater Avallaunius, as Machen chose to call himself, entered the Isis-Urania Temple of the Hermetic Order of the Golden Dawn and signed his name on the Order Roll – the last Neophyte to do so before the expulsion of Mathers and his cronies. Initially, as he recalled in his autobiography, *Things Near and Far* (1923), the Order helped him:

> I must confess that it did me a great deal of good – for the time. To stand waiting at a closed door in a breathless expectation, to see it open suddenly and disclose two figures in a habit that I never thought to see worn by the living, to catch for a moment the vision of a cloud of incense smoke and certain dim lights glimmering in it before the bandage was put over the eyes and the arm felt a firm grasp upon it that led the hesitating footsteps into the unknown darkness: all this was strange and admirable indeed; and strange to think that within a foot or two of those closely curtained windows the common life of London moved on the common pavement, as supremely unaware of what was being done within an arm's length as if our works had been the works of the other side of the moon.

But whatever the Golden Dawn did for Machen's peace of mind, it did nothing for his soul: 'But as for anything vital in the secret order, for anything that mattered two straws to any reasonable being, there was nothing in it, and less than nothing . . .

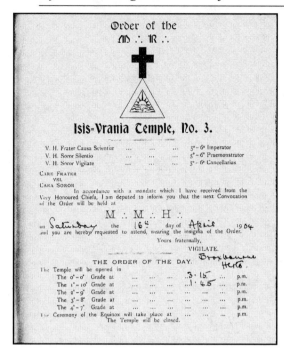

*Printed summons to a meeting of Waite's Independent and Rectified Rite.*

the society as a society was pure foolishness concerned with impotent and imbecile Abracadabras. It knew nothing whatever about anything and concealed the fact under an impressive ritual and a sonorous phraseology.' All in all, Machen felt it 'shed no ray of any kind on my path'.

And yet he was caught up in the strife of 1900. On 5 May, Machen, by now a 3 = 8 Practicus, attended a meeting of the Order at which the members present, including Waite, accepted the new constitution and pledged allegiance to their new rulers. Among them was W.B. Yeats, who had been elected Imperator of Isis-Urania.

It was about this time that Yeats told Machen of the battle with Crowley and the threats that followed it. As recounted by Machen, it makes a picturesque tale:

> I was once talking to a dark young man, of quiet and retiring
> aspect, who wore glasses – he and I had met at a place
> where we had to be blindfolded before we could see the
> light – and he told me a queer tale of the manner in which

his life was in daily jeopardy. He described the doings of a fiend in human form, a man who was well known to be an expert in Black Magic, a man who hung up naked women in cupboards by hooks which pierced the flesh of their arms. This monster – I may say that there is such a person, though I can by no means go bail for the actuality of any of the misdeeds charged against him – had, for some reason which I do not recollect, taken a dislike to my dark young friend. In consequence, so I was assured, he had hired a gang in Lambeth, who were grievously to maim or preferably to slaughter the dark young man; each member of the gang receiving a retaining fee of eight shillings and sixpence – a sum, by the way, that sounds as if it were the face value of some mediaeval coin long obsolete. I listened in wonder, for there are some absurdities so enormous that they seem to have a stunning effect on the common sense, paralysing it for the moment and inhibiting its action. It was only when I got home that it dawned upon me that I had been listening to the Young Man in Spectacles, and that he came out of 'The Three Impostors'.

On re-reading his *Shadows of Life and Thought,* 40 years after these events, Machen wrote to Waite to ask him about the Young Man in Spectacles. 'I have no notion of whether he be alive or dead,' he remarked, 'I have forgotten his very name.' To such an extent had Machen passed out of the Golden Dawn.

Waite, on the other hand, never really left the Order. His attitude towards it was much the same as Machen's. Rather than leave it he determined to change it. As the reconstituted Order fell into bickering factions, Waite lay low and waited for his time to come. He prepared the ground well. On 19 September 1901 he had been initiated into Freemasonry, and in the following April he entered the S.R.I.A., where Westcott and so many of the more important Golden Dawn adepts were still to be found. He also remained on friendly terms with Yeats, working with him, albeit inconclusively, on the 'Ritual Sub-Committee' for the revision of the 2 = 9 Theoricus ritual. Then, at the Order's Annual General Meeting on 2 May, 1903, Waite made his first move, upsetting Brodie-Innes' (the 'poor small pope of Edinburgh' as Waite called him) attempt to seize control, and insisting on a return to a triad of Chiefs, all of whom must be Masons. After months of wrangling, the Order simply broke in two. A sizeable minority followed Waite (and in so doing utterly eschewed magic), while most of the remainder followed Dr Felkin and re-named their part of the Order the Stella Matutina. A few simply cast the dust of the Order from their feet and cursed both houses.

Machen, as one might expect, went with Waite, but more for the sake of friendship than from a commitment to the Order. He attended few meetings of the 'Independent and Rectified Rite' and eventually severed his connection altogether. Unlike Waite, he had no desire to write or to rewrite rituals. He remained an enthusiastic literary partner and happily wrote his share of the letters that built up into their curious, privately printed book *The House of the Hidden Light* (1904).

This literary conceit recounted, in veiled form, Machen's and Waite's escapades with their lady friends during 1900 and 1901. The text is constructed around the imaginary rites of a non-existent 'Secret Order of the Dawn'. It is filled with obscure references to the real Golden Dawn, both by Waite:

> It is common knowledge that there was a reformation in the days of the Friary, through a certain transitional change in the substance of the world, which exhaled sorcery, and all external things put on the proportion of magic, as the hierophant assumes his vestments to open the Lodge of the Adepts. But after that there was darkness, and many Kings died upon their thrones. And now the *nova reformatio* is like a second step taken in a Lodge of the Adepts when the face of the Neophyte is turned to the Grand East.

and by Machen:

> They must be fixed by the Operation of the Sages, so that from dead stones they may be changed into Living Philosophical Pillars, that they may stand forever in our House as the Pillars of I and B stand in the Temple of the Masons. It is, perhaps, on this account that our Fraternity has been variously hinted at by the phrases – 'Adepts of Fire and

of Water', those who 'Work with Fire and Water', or again the 'Children of A and W'. For we are called 'Those that are Redeemed of Earth, and have passed through the Region of the Air' (which is the world of sorcery, of the year of our wonder), and henceforth we dwell in and work with these two most excellent elements, which are the Beginning and the End, the two opposites which must at last be reconciled: 'When the King comes forth from Avalon'.

Waite's preference for a mystical, as opposed to a magical, purpose in ritual was also made clear in his poetry. His long verse drama *The Book of the King's Dole* (in *Strange Houses of Sleep* 1906) begins with an account of 'The Ceremony of Opening the Chantry' which includes this description:

> The entrance at the imputed West of the Chancel is guarded by two Great Pillars, inscribed in the tongue of men and angels, with the respective words MERCY and SEVERITY. The broad intervening space is taken up by the five steps of the chancel, but ingress is not attained, except at need by the Epopts, through the Rood-Screen betwixt the Pillars, as the column inscribed Severity is the place of Indulgence by which admission is given from without.

> At the imputed East behind the altar there is a heavy curtain embroidered with figures of palm-trees. A certain natural light filters through the Chantry, but it is tinged and transmuted by intermediaries of coloured glass and by emblazonments in the great windows North and South, belonging to the body of the Church. An enormous Tau Cross lies upon the Chancel steps, but there is no figure of man extended thereon.

Nor is this merely the vault of the adepts brought to church, for it can also be seen as a description (completed later in the poem) of two of the trumps – the High Priestess and the Hanged Man – from Waite's Tarot pack, drawn for him by Pamela Colman Smith. She had dutifully followed him into the Independent and Rectified Rite.

Within the Order, the old Golden Dawn rituals had been set aside and new versions developed by Waite. In 1910 these were printed and although used also by the members of the Stella Matutina (of which Yeats was a member), it is unlikely that the new 2 = 9 Theoricus Ritual, owed anything at all to Yeats' earlier attempts at revision. When the Hierophant explains the meaning of the Cubical Cross it is Waite alone who speaks:

> The Cubical Cross is composed of 22 squares, which have several symbolical attributions; but at this stage of your progress you should regard them as more especially referring to the letters of the Hebrew alphabet, which are inscribed thereon, and in this manner to the intimations of that Divine Word of which the expressed word is the reflection and echo from far away, even as behind the logical understanding and the natural mind of man, there is realisation after another mode. The Word in transcendence is represented on earth by silence rather than by the uttered voice; it is breathed into all things and is the Divine Immanence in all; it is in earth, air, water and fire, corresponding to the parts of our personality or the four utterances of the Sacred Word in man; it is the Constellations of the Zodiac as the testimony of all that is visible to all that is unseen.

And even this was too close to the original for Waite. Four years later, while the Stella Matutina flourished, the Independent and Rectified Rite was riven by 'Internecine feuds on the authenticity of documents' and Waite 'withdrew his copyright Rituals and dissolved the Rite as at that time constituted'. When his new Order, the Fellowship of the Rosy Cross, came into being in the following year (1915), its constitution made clear its approach. One clause stated that 'The Order of the Rosy Cross has no concern whatsoever in occult or psychical research: it is a Quest of Grace and not a Quest of Power'. Another, which referred to 'Separated Temples', stated firmly that 'The Independent and Rectified Rite, with its dependencies, if any, in so far as now in activity, and the Stella Matutina Temple, together with its dependencies, are not in communion with the Fellowship of the Rosy Cross, and cannot be Visited or Joined'. For Waite the old Order had indeed passed away.

*Waite as Imperator of his own later Order, the Fellowship of the Rosy Cross, which he established in 1915. The drawing by John Trinick, a member of the F.R.C., was used as a frontispiece to Waite's* New Encyclopaedia of Freemasonry *(1921).*

# W.B. Yeats

Just as Waite rejected magic and drove it from the rituals of both the Outer and Inner Orders of his reconstructed Golden Dawn, so Yeats accepted it and strove to preserve the magical purity of the original Golden Dawn. Magic was essential to his world-view. Not the magic of Mathers' obsessions, nor the ritual ravings of Crowley, but the power of imagination and the interaction of minds. Yeats set out his magical beliefs for all to see in his essay 'Magic', that appeared in 1901:

> I believe in the practice and philosophy of what we have agreed to call magic, in what I must call the evocation of spirits, though I do not know what they are, in the power

175

*William Butler Yeats (1865–1939), photographed in his study in Woburn Buildings in 1904. This portrait was printed in* The Tatler *in June of that year.*

of creating magical illusions, in the visions of truth in the depths of the mind when the eyes are closed; and I believe in three doctrines, which have, as I think, been handed down from early times, and been the foundations of nearly all magical practices. These doctrines are:-

(1) That the borders of our mind are ever shifting, and that many minds can flow into one another, as it were, and create or reveal a single mind, a single energy.

(2) That the borders of our memories are as shifting, and that our memories are a part of one great memory, the memory of Nature herself.

(3) That this great mind and great memory can be evoked by symbols.

Earlier in the same year he had explained his ideas privately, in greater detail and in greater earnest, to his fellow adepts of the R.R. et A.C. 'The central principle of all the Magic of power,' he told them, 'is that everything we formulate in the

*Yeats' entry in the Golden Dawn Address Book. He entered the Order on 7 March 1890, taking the motto 'Demon Est Deus Inversus'.*

imagination, if we formulate it strongly enough, realises itself in the circumstances of life, acting either through our own souls, or through the spirits of nature.'

But Yeats was not concerned solely with the instruction of his fellows: he was concerned also for the very survival of the Order. The controversy over the groups had come to a head, with Annie Horniman's and his own bitter opposition to Florence Farr and her colleagues. Yeats had already issued three open 'Letters to the Adepti', on what he called 'the present crisis', setting out in detail his reasons for objecting to group working. They were, however, to no avail, for the ruling Council of the Second Order rejected his complaints and supported the Groups. Yeats promptly resigned as Imperator of Isis-Urania, and in March 1901, wrote his pamphlet *Is the Order of R.R. et A.C. to remain a Magical Order?*, following it with a *Postscript* two months later.

In his pamphlet, Yeats argued for 'strict obedience to the

laws and by-laws', a return to the system of progress by examinations, and an acceptance of the pre-eminence of those possessed of the higher adept grades. Progress in the Order, he argued,

> is not merely an ascent, that has for symbols the climbing of the Serpent through the Tree of Life and of the Adepti through the Degrees that we know of, but a descent that is symbolised by the Lightning Flash among the sacred leaves, and that should be symbolised, if the Order has not abandoned an essential part of its ritual, by the obligation spoken on the day of Corpus Christi by some senior in the name of the Third Order, which thereby takes upon itself the sins of all the Fratres and Sorores, as wisdom takes upon itself the sins of the world.

And a strict hierarchy is necessary for this symbolic vicarious sacrifice to have any merit, otherwise the Third Order will not 'gather up into its strength'. A group frailty, he maintained, 'must bear the burdens of frailty'. All of this would aid in holding the Order together, which, he believed, was important because:

> If we preserve the unity of the Order, if we make that unity efficient among us, the Order will become a single very powerful talisman, creating in us, and in the world about us, such moods and circumstances as may best serve the magical life, and best awaken the magical wisdom.

Despite this impassioned appeal, the squabbling went on and the fractured Order proved irreparable. In the immediate aftermath of the turmoil of 1903 Yeats stayed aloof. As Waite put it, in a report to his own followers, 'The V.H. Frater D.E.D.I. moving from place to place and his views for the most part unknown'. Eventually he joined forces with Dr Felkin in the Amoun Temple of the Stella Matutina, collecting his Theoricus Adeptus Minor sub-grade in 1912 and advancing to the 6 = 5 Grade of Adeptus Major in 1914. And for all that he claimed in 1915 (in the first draft of his autobiography) that 'I attend but little', he was Imperator of Amoun Temple from 1914 to 1922,

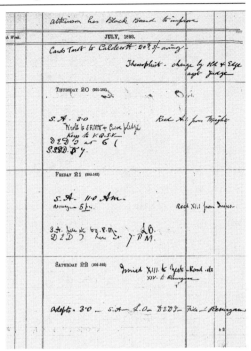

*Second Order members carried out their magical work at the vault at Clipstone Street. They recorded their attendance in the Order Diary. Yeats was a regular attendee, recording his presence on 20 and 21 July 1893.*

and left only when the Order 'ended amid quarrels caused by men, otherwise worthy, who claimed a Rosicrucian sanction for their fantasies'.

His career in the Order had been longer than that of almost any other: Frater Demon Est Deus Inversus had come to the Golden Dawn from the Theosophical Society, entering the Order as a Neophyte on 7 March, 1890 and not in 1887 as he himself stated. He worked industriously within it, although the only Outer Order office he took up was that of Stolistes in 1892. He attained the grade of Adeptus Minor in June of 1893. On occasions he stayed with the Mathers in Paris, noticing that Mathers 'was drinking too much neat brandy, though not to drunkenness' and doubting whether the self-styled MacGregor 'had seen the Highlands, or even, until invited there by some White Rose Society, Scotland itself'. Once he acted as Hegemon at a meeting of the Ahathoor Temple, probably in hopes of seeing Maude Gonne, the great love of his life, but she, Soror Per

Ignem ad Lucem, was absent, 'on the point of leaving Paris for a short time'. Yeats was disappointed.

He yet worked consistently to preserve the Order in its original purity, but what he really believed concerning the Anna Sprengel letters and the cipher manuscripts he never made clear. His conversations with Westcott in 1900 about these documents were inconclusive. His knowledge of occultism was valued within the Stella Matutina, where he was not only Imperator of Amoun, but also Instructor in Ancient Traditions. These 'traditions' may have included astrology and the Tarot, for he had progressed far in his understanding of all the varied branches of the Order's wisdom.

His knowledge stood him in good stead. Whatever else the Golden Dawn may have done for Yeats, we who read him should be grateful that it inspired his strange and wonderful metaphysical study, *A Vision*. In the book's dedication (to Mina Mathers), he finally explained what it was that he had sought in the Order:

> Some were looking for spiritual happiness or for some form of unknown power, but I had a practical object. I wished for a system of thought that would leave my imagination free to create as it chose and yet make all that it created, or could create, part of the one history, and that the soul's.

Perhaps in the end, he found it.

# CHAPTER SEVEN

# The Lightning-Struck Tower: Life among the Ruins

If there was one reason for Yeats' leaving the Stella Matutina, it was Miss Christina Mary Stoddart, otherwise Soror Il Faut Chercher, who had been 'for some years a Ruling Chief of the Mother Temple of the Stella Matutina and R.R. et A.C.'. Miss Stoddart was as passionate and paranoid a believer in the Secret Chiefs as was Mathers, but her view of them was quite different. If other renegades from the Stella Matutina were responsible for the awe in which the Order is held by simple-minded, latter-day occultists, then she was the fountain-head of the lunatic image of the Order, a model for today's self-styled 'Born-again Christians'. Throughout its history there were many eccentrics for whom the Golden Dawn acted as a lodestone and whose lives were, for good or ill, moulded by the Order. But Miss Stoddart was unique in being motivated by a fanatical hatred of the Order she had once loved. She was also a very efficient publicist.

After the alarms and diversions of 1900, the Golden Dawn was split into two warring camps. On the one hand was Mathers, his subservient wife and the Ahathoor Temple, supported by Crowley, Berridge and the few adepts who remained, as they perversely expressed it, 'loyal'. On the other was Yeats, Florence Farr and the overwhelming majority of members of the R.R. et A.C. who could no longer tolerate Mathers' bombastic behaviour. Firmly on the fence, but with sympathetic gestures to one side or the other as it suited him, was Dr Westcott. And then came the Horos trial.

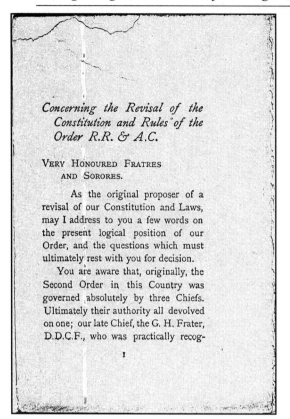

*Concerning the Revisal of the*
*Constitution and Rules of the*
*Order R.R. & A.C.*

VERY HONOURED FRATRES
AND SORORES.

As the original proposer of a
revisal of our Constitution and Laws,
may I address to you a few words on
the present logical position of our
Order, and the questions which must
ultimately rest with you for decision.

You are aware that, originally, the
Second Order in this Country was
governed absolutely by three Chiefs.
Ultimately their authority all devolved
on one; our late Chief, the G. H. Frater,
D.D.C.F., who was practically recog-

I

*Brodie-Innes' pamphlet*
Concerning the Revisal of
the Constitution,
*circulated in 1902.*

At once the Golden Dawn ceased to be. Its place was taken
by Mathers' Alpha et Omega, and by the London adepts'
Morgen Rothe, both shedding members as the terror of
ridicule, or worse, struck at middle-class sensitivity. Among
them was William Peck, the City Astronomer of Edinburgh.
'Peck was in a ghastly funk over the Horos affair', wrote Westcott
to Gardner in 1902, 'and hurriedly burnt all his lectures, letters,
jewels, robes etc.'. For those who remained, further division
awaited.

By the end of 1903, the rows in Isis-Urania had led to the
formation of both Felkin's Stella Matutina and Waite's
Independent and Rectified Rite. They were utterly opposed in
esoteric outlook but united in their hostility to Mathers. For
some years a concordat was maintained between the two

*Application form for the Order of the M[orgen] R[othe], later known as the Independent and Rectified Rite. The applicant was the masonic writer, W.L. Wilmshurst.*

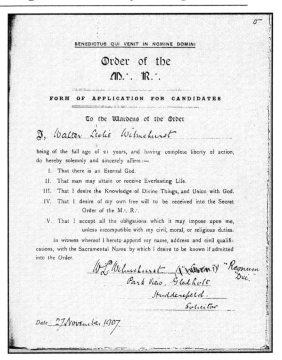

Orders. By 1912, Felkin was working, more or less openly, with J.W. Brodie-Innes, who had revived the Amen-Ra Temple at Edinburgh and was maintaining friendly relations with both Mathers and Westcott. This was more than Waite would tolerate and the concordat came to an end, followed in 1914 by the Independent and Rectified Rite itself, whose members were beginning to seek the magic that Waite had rejected – only to find themselves also rejected.

These renegade members of Waite's Order, Mrs Rand (Vigilate) and the Revd. A.H.E. Lee (Hilarion) amongst them, did not at first join the Stella Matutina, but retained a form of 'continuing' Independent and Rectified Rite. Most of them drifted gradually into Co-Masonry, presumably wishing to retain Waite's masonic ethos but not to lose the ladies. Most also remained on friendly terms with Waite himself. The Revd. Lee, who included six of Waite's poems in his *Oxford Book of English Mystical Verse*, encouraged the young Charles Williams to visit Waite and thus brought about Williams' 12 years' membership of the Fellowship of the Rosy Cross.

They were, too, a far cry from the self-centred moral pygmies who made up the membership of Aleister Crowley's Argentinum Astrum, the aberrant version of the Golden Dawn that he launched in 1907. One member, at least, had been active in the old Order. Elaine Simpson, Soror Fidelis (strictly: Donorum Dei Dispensatio Fidelis), had sided with Mathers in 1900, but soon afterwards had left for the Far East. She kept her dedication to magic, however, and in 1906 worked diligently with Crowley at Shanghai in the magical evocation of Aiwass, his twisted inner self. It thus seems unlikely that she was, as Israel Regardie believed, merely an 'incurable poseur'. 'There is one rumour', he wrote in *My Rosicrucian Adventure*, 'of a certain Soror F. who donned her full Adept regalia for the purpose of attending a fancy dress ball.' Crowley saw nothing wrong in this. In his copy of Regardie's book he merely noted in the margin, 'Fidelis. In Hong Kong. She wrote to me about it herself. She took a prize'. But in the tale of the Golden Dawn, Crowley is a side-show and we must return to the centre of the stage.

After 1915, there were some half-a-dozen offshoots of the original Golden Dawn, but only two were of real consequence. The first of these, Waite's Fellowship of the Rosy Cross, had separated itself completely from the old traditions of the Order, and fascinating though the story of the Salvator Mundi Temple is – with Charles Williams playing a prominent role and Algernon Blackwood maintaining at least a nominal membership – it has no significant place in the story of the Golden Dawn. The spirit of the Order persisted rather in the Stella Matutina.

If Dr Robert William Felkin had a besetting sin, it was his absolute conviction that the Secret Chiefs not only existed in the flesh, but that he could and would meet them. In this context his very choice of motto is instructive. When he entered the Amen-Ra Temple in March 1894, he took the name Finem Respice (Have regard to the End) – the very motto inscribed on the one reputed portrait of Christian Rosencreutz. During the years before the First World War he travelled much about

*Aleister Crowley (1875–1947), as he appeared in 1910 after a decade away from the Golden Dawn.*

Germany seeking the true Vault of the Adepts but found only Rudolf Steiner's far from ancient Rosicrucian society. Felkin nonetheless convinced himself that he had met Anna Sprengel's niece (he did meet an Anna Sprengel, but she professed no connection with the mysterious lady adept) and that he had tracked down the Order that lay behind the Golden Dawn.

He was also convinced that he was receiving astral messages from a disembodied Arabian adept, one Ara ben Shemesh, and his 'Sun Masters', Felkin also derived material derived from the astral teachers of Brodie-Innes' 'Solar Order'. According to Miss Stoddart these 'Sun Masters' demanded that Felkin and his fellow Chiefs sign a pledge, part of which ran as follows:

> I declare in the presence and in the name of all I hold most awful and sacred, that I fully believe in the genuineness of the messages and communications, the teachings and the rituals of the Order of the Stella Matutina. That I know not, neither will I seek to know, how the same are transmitted or

185

received, but I will receive them without question from their appointed medium, and that if hereafter I am assailed by doubt, I will reveal such doubt only to the Masters. I will in no case ever attempt, directly or indirectly, to destroy or weaken the faith of any other, but on the contrary will attempt to remove doubts and confirm faith.

Such a commitment led at once to self-perpetuating credulity on Felkin's part.

Among the more choice of the Masters' subsequent messages was this one on the role of the Order after the ending of the war:

> Our function is to direct the new life which will spring up when present disturbances have cleared the ground; it is as if a giant harrow were passing over the face of the world, and when that is done those like us must be ready *to sow the seed.* This war was an inevitable means of destroying the old order of things to make room for the new; that already the ideas of peace and unity have been implanted, but they could not spread freely until the old had been broken asunder. It is the 'Tower struck by Lightning' – the 'Rending Asunder of the Veil'.

To Miss Stoddart, this somewhat fatuous message was an anathema. Her chauvinistic spirit bridled at its vile internationalism.

There were also 'spirit visions' on the part of Order members who saw the Secret Chiefs in their hidden sanctuary. The Chiefs seemed invariably to be Arabic or Jewish and thus fed Miss Stoddart's growing anti-Semitic fantasies. By 1919 she was having such visions herself, and while at Church that Easter, she 'saw in place of the altar the great Vault of the Inner Order, into which the Twelve Brethren, in black habits with cowls over their heads, were hurriedly entering'. She then saw 'a dazzling light' and 'a sharp pain seized the heart'. Rather than suspect an attack of migraine, she attributed this to the 'Black Rosicrucians'. Felkin, to whom she wrote for advice, in New Zealand where he had settled in 1916, suggested that 'instead of fearing imaginary black Rosicrucians in Germany or elsewhere', she should 'consciously endeavour to co-operate with the true Rosicrucians who do undoubtedly exist'.

But it was too late. To Miss Stoddart, now Soror Het Ta in her role as Ruling Chief of the Order, all these astral entities were evil and it was her duty to oppose them. She never once questioned their objective reality. Thus it was that she set about systematically wrecking the Stella Matutina, or rather, trying to wreck it – as we shall see there were others equally keen to save it. For four years she laboured at her *Investigations into the Foundations of the Order G.D. and R.R. et A.C. and the Source of its Teachings,* an inner history of the Stella Matutina in which she concluded that the Order was inherently evil. Later she rewrote the text for inclusion in her book *Light Bearers of Darkness* (1930) where her paranoid fantasies were given free rein. The book proved a godsend to fanatical anti-Semites who were already baying for occultists' blood and who saw occultism as the work of a Jewish cabal bent on the destruction of Christian civilisation.

Felkin attempted to reason with her, but in July 1920 reluctantly accepted her impending resignation from the Order. He commiserated with her over the endemic squabbling in the Order:

> I fear that your remarks about the long fight against disloyalty, jealousy etc. are quite true. I had hoped that they were ended before I left London, but I was very badly mistaken. I also agree that the Evil Powers are pleased at this.

And he protested against her imputation of wickedness behind the Order:

> You surely cannot say that the matters of a serious nature that have happened since my departure have anything to do with Order teaching or its origin?

But she did so say and the Order was diminished by the loss of a Ruling Chief, and yet, paradoxically, it was the squabbling and the breaking into factions that ensured the Order's survival. There were so many purely human Chiefs with inordinate amounts of vanity that the continuation of pieces of the old Order, however minuscule, was guaranteed.

Public attacks on the Golden Dawn also continued, however, although they called forth some spirited replies. They were nothing new, for the public had been aware of the Order (or would have been if they had bothered to look) since its inception and members were used to occasional derisory comments in the press.

In 1889, following a somewhat acrimonious correspondence about a spurious Rosicrucian Society, Westcott placed the following pompous announcement in the pages of *Lucifer*:

### The Hermetic Students of the Rosicrucian G.D. in the Outer

The chiefs of the Second Order, fearing that the proceedings of certain men in the Northern Counties of England may by exhibition of pretended powers and Rosicrucian dignities lead students away from the Higher Paths of Mysticism, into Goetic practices, desire that all Fratres and Sorores of the G.D. will accordingly warn the unwary and uninitiated that no such persons hold any warrant from us, nor possess our ancient and secret knowledge.

Given forth from the M . ˙ . A . ˙ .

of

Sapiens dominabitur Astris

Dec duce comite ferro

Non omnis moriar

Vincit omnis veritas

Published by order of the above: Sapere Aude: Cancellarius in Londinense.

The popular press missed this opportunity to ridicule the Order, and since there was a flurry of new members at the end of 1889, the announcement achieved its object.

Further reference to the Order came in Waite's *Unknown*

*World,* and more amusingly in the Revd. C.M. Davies 'auto-biographical 'record of 40 years' experience in the modern mystery', *The Great Secret* (1895), where he wrote:

> There is, in fact, a secret society working at this very time in the great Metropolis, under the auspices of a man in a somewhat prominent public position. I am not an initiate; but there are a great many ladies in its ranks; and ladies, as we know, will talk. They profess to have devised adequate safeguards for the practice of black magic; but the little I know of this fraternity – against whom I have nothing to say – confirms the opinion drawn from my own slender experience, and leads me to quote, for the benefit of such as are inclined to go in for black magic, Punch's historic advice to young men about to marry: *'Don't'.*

One lady had indeed talked: his wife, Anna Jane, who had entered the Order in 1891, and risen to become an Adeptus Minor but resigned in 1894. It is intriguing to speculate just what she told him.

The Horos trial, of course, gave detailed and unwanted exposure and brought ridicule in its train. It was followed by Berridge's court case and then in March 1905 even more sensationally on the front pages of the *Weekly Dispatch* where the Golden Dawn (as the 'A.O.') was paraded before the public in the course of a breach of promise action against the Marquis Townshend.

Mrs Evelyn Sheffield (Soror Vires Animat Veritas) had brought an action against the Marquis Townshend which commenced on 23 February 1905, only to withdraw the action suddenly and dramatically the following morning, as Mrs Sheffield had learned that the defence intended to parade her membership of the Order before the court. Determined that the public should know the truth, the noble reporters of the *Dispatch* dug deep and rattled money until 'a former member of the society' provided them with all the details. The Pledge Form was printed in full, Mathers' and Westcott's addresses were published and a description of the supposed Neophyte ritual was given:

**He was led by the High Priestess, clad in flowing draperies,**

into a chamber and blindfolded. The odour of incense blended with the fragrance of flowers. The two walked on over a thick, soft carpet and then halted. The bandage was removed from his eyes, and he stood before the High Priest, who sat on a throne, wearing the robes of his priestly office, and beckoned him to kneel.

This he did, the while ten girls, roughly described in the ritual as 'the ten virgins' advanced in the flimsiest silks and arranged themselves around him. Then was brought in a white dove, which was killed and the blood sprinkled over the initiate. After this the 'virgins' danced for several minutes, the oath of secrecy was taken, he made his vow of allegiance, and the ceremony was over.

Rather than ignore all this nonsense, Mathers rose to the bait. He wrote a furious letter of protest to the newspaper and a reporter went to interview him at Acton where he was then staying. As was inevitable, he was made to seem a fool when the interview was reported. There were references to his 'exaggerated dignity', to his 'pince-nez glasses' and to his 'jewelled snake rings on nearly all the fingers of his left hand'. He was quoted as saying 'Your article contains a lot of preposterous rubbish, sir!', but his defence did little to quash the earlier query in the *Dispatch* as to whether society should permit the activities of

this extraordinary society, with its strange passwords, its mysterious gestures, its gibberish of dead languages, and the pseudo sciences, its sumptuous feastings and its gorgeous ceremonials, its quaint rites and its very insistent demands upon the Neophytes among its members.

Mathers had also taken Westcott's name in vain and the reporter also called upon 'Mr Wynn Westcott'. As an accomplished prevaricator, Westcott denied any connection with the affair, stating that 'I severed my connection with the society ten years ago'. He further denied having seen or heard from Mathers over the same ten years. How he afterwards salved his conscience remains unknown.

After this case, the members of the Golden Dawn had a five-year respite until Crowley published the rituals of the Order in *The Equinox* and Mathers unwisely gave them further publicity with his attempts at suppressing the journal. But still there was no real condemnation of the Order. That would not come until the spectre of anti-Semitism arose in the aftermath of the Great War.

In July 1920, a series of articles in *The Morning Post* attacked Freemasonry as an agent of a Jewish-Bolshevik plot to overthrow the West. By implication, all occult orders deriving from Masonry were also subversive and dangerous. This poisonous rubbish was immediately rebutted in detail by A.E. Waite. But the author of the articles, Mrs Nesta Webster, went on to produce an alarming work on *Secret Societies and Subversive Movements*. She gave a succinct account of the Golden Dawn (using pseudonyms and altering the name of the Order) which she had evidently received from Miss Stoddart. She suggested that there were in Britain occult groups which 'practise rites and evocations that lead to illness, moral perversion, mental derangement, and even in some cases to death'. She went on to quote approvingly Miss Stoddart's conviction that 'the Order is being controlled by some Sun Order after the nature of the Illuminati, if not by that Order itself'. And then followed the inevitable conclusion:

> **How in the face of these declarations, coming from those inside the movement, can anyone maintain that Illuminism is dead and that secret societies present no danger to Christian civilisation?**

Fortunately, her words fell upon deaf ears, and even when Miss Stoddart's own book appeared, under the pseudonym of Inquire Within, public reaction was sceptical – if only because most normal citizens couldn't believe that the 'Sun Masters' existed at all, and thus could see no threat from them. Members of the Order yet tried to limit the book's circulation. Dr Carnegie Dickson, one of the most active later members of the Stella Matutina, wrote to John Watkins, the occult bookseller, in the hope that 'you will put the book on your "Index

Expurgatorius" along with the works of Crowley and other such undesirable persons'. There is no evidence that Mr Watkins did ban the book, but he kept the letter which contains a fascinating account of Carnegie Dickson's opinion of his former Chief:

> She very much overdid her Occult studies, against his advice, and, very largely, owing to her time of life, according to Dr Felkin, she entirely lost her mental balance. I am told by some mutual friends with whom she stayed at that time, that she was in the condition of a 'raving lunatic', and someone had constantly to be in the same room with her at night. We were all very sorry for her, and also much grieved that (as is common in such cases) she turned against all her old friends, especially poor Dr Felkin, whom she has been constantly attacking ever since.

He concluded his letter by saying that, 'I should think that very few people will bother to read the book, and it is best treated with the silence of contempt. We are all loyal British subjects, who look, with horror and loathing upon Bolshevism and all its works.' But only Waite had attacked her anti-Semitism.

Hard on Miss Stoddart's heels came the posthumous work of Lady Queenborough, *Occult Theocrasy*, issued in Paris in 1933. This hysterical work says little about either the Golden Dawn or the Stella Matutina, save to refer without elaboration to 'some of its shameful practices' and to state (while acknowledging Miss Stoddart as a source!) that the heads of the Stella Matutina were Aleister Crowley and William Wynn Westcott. As the book attacks Jews, freemasons and Roman Catholics with equal gusto it has reappeared in print for the edification of that minority of the American Moral Majority who have learned how to read. There has, as yet, arisen nothing to supersede it.

For all their credulity, most 'men (and women) in the street' prefer to believe that occultists are mostly benign, and their beliefs have been assiduously reinforced by members and quasi-members of the Order with a penchant for fiction, and especially for tales of 'psychic detectives'. The first of these was Algernon Blackwood (Frater Umbram Fugat Veritas), whose

*John Silence: Physician Extraordinary* (1908) was clearly modelled on the book's dedicatee: 'M.L.W. The original of John Silence and my companion in many adventures'. No known member has initials (either of his name or motto) that correspond in any way and it is probable that he had no connection with the Order, but supplied a physical frame into which Blackwood fed the occult characteristics:

> To look at – he was now past forty – he was sparely built, with speaking brown eyes in which shone the light of knowledge and self-confidence . . . A close beard concealed the mouth without disguising the grim determination of lips and jaw, and the face somehow conveyed an impression of transparency, almost of light, so delicately were the features refined away.

The artist's impression on the cover of the book suggests no one so much as J.W. Brodie-Innes but he remains a most unlikely candidate.

John Silence battles equally, and always successfully, against ghosts and elementals. His abilities come from having 'submitted himself to a long and severe training, at once physical, mental and spiritual'. But he uses no overt rituals and has none of the trappings of the magician. He is, as his evil adversaries realise, 'A man of power . . . A man of God!' He would, one feels, be more use against such foes than the theatrical Dr Taverner of Dion Fortune's amazing stories.

He, at least, was based on an identifiable original: Theodore Moriarty, who was involved with the young Dion Fortune at the Medico-Psychological Clinic, described in her *Psychic Self-Defence*. Whether Moriarty (who certainly believed that he disposed of unwelcome and dangerous occult entities) ever acted out the rituals performed by Dr Taverner is another matter. The fictional magician, dressed in his 'great cope', 'emerald green soutane' with a 'jewelled clasp upon his breast' and wearing 'the Head-dress of Egypt' while bearing a jewelled ankh, is unlikely to have been matched by his pragmatic counterpart in the real world. But he was matched by later fictional copies: both the gallant white magician, Miles Pennoyer of Margery Lawrence's *Number Seven Queer Street*, and the evil Canon Copely-Syle of Dennis Wheatley's *To the Devil a Daughter* maintained ritual (if not, in the latter case, moral) propriety. And all such fictions have been perennially popular.

Nor, if some magicians are to be believed, is real life much less dramatic. Much of the modern success of the diluted offshoots of the Golden Dawn is due to the prolific and breathless writing of Violet Firth, under her pen-name (derived from her motto of 'Deo Non Fortuna') of Dion Fortune. The story of her adventures in the Order has already been told. Her books are still published, and her Order, the Fraternity of the Inner Light, still flourishes. But her most far-reaching effort was her review article, 'Ceremonial Magic Unveiled', printed in the *Occult Review* for January 1933. In this – ostensibly a review of Israel Regardie's two books, *The Garden of Pomegranates* and *The Tree of Life* – she exposed more of the nature of the Golden Dawn, and to a wider audience, than had been done by anyone before. She pointed out that it still existed:

> [Regardie] is also incorrect when he says that the 'Golden Dawn' is defunct; it has broken up into various scattered units, of varying degrees of efficiency, but I know personally, of four functioning Lodges, all of which have got the full set of rites and teaching; and there are quite likely to be others of which I do not know.

More than this, she related her own experiences with Mina Mathers, and went on to state that, 'It seems to me that whoever can work the system of the "Golden Dawn" in such a manner as to pick up the contacts of the Secret Chiefs need not pay very much attention to the "Trespassers will be prosecuted" boards put up on the physical plane by persons who are not altogether disinterested'. The system, she added, 'when worked by competent persons, is effectual, whether they are chartered or not'. But she stressed the dangers to the incompetent practitioner and urged that the initiation rites and magical formulae should still be kept secret.

*Israel Regardie (1907–85) published his massive four-volume work,* The Golden Dawn *between 1936 and 1940. In it he revealed the inner workings of the Order.*

But it was encouragement enough for Regardie. The members of the Stella Matutina Temples might fume – and those of Hermes Temple at Bristol, of which he was a member, in particular – but he was determined to persist in his grand design of publishing the entire corpus of Golden Dawn rituals and teaching. Four years after Dion Fortune's article appeared, the first volume of *The Golden Dawn: an account of the Teachings, Rites and Ceremonies of the Order of the Golden Dawn* was published in Chicago, to be followed in successive years by three further volumes. It was as complete an exposition of the whole system as any would-be magician could wish for. Despite their theoretical objections (he had, after all, breached his solemn Obligation) members of the Order took it up thankfully – for it saved an inordinate amount of time that would have been spent in the copying of Grade and other rituals.

Regardie justified the breaking of his oath by referring to

the work of Paul Foster Case: 'He has', said Regardie (in 'Why I wrote *The Golden Dawn*), 'violated every clause of his obligation. In the first place, he has formed a schismatic body using Golden Dawn ritual. And secondly, he distributes Tarot and kabbalistic knowledge based upon Order teaching to anyone who applies for it. Yet this is the sort of person who impugns my motives, attacks my scheme of open presentation of worthwhile knowledge, and upholds the sanctity of obligations and secrecy!' More generally, he argued that:

> The truth is that the present-day Chiefs had become afraid of Magic. They felt disinclined to distribute the necessary esoteric teaching concerning it. Thus they had *violated* the intention of the foundation of the Order which was to teach the way of attainment by Magic. Thus, by their actions, they have abrogated the validity of my obligation.

While this argument may be neither valid nor true as to its propositions, it did state one fact: the Chiefs of the Stella Matutina would not publish the teaching of the Golden Dawn. Very well, then, if they wouldn't, Regardie would. And he did.

In this way the moribund Order was revived. There was, admittedly, one thriving temple in New Zealand: Smaragdum Thalasses, which Felkin had founded in 1912 and which, by diligence and good fortune, survived under the name of Whare Ra until the 1970s. All the others were declining and decaying. Regardie's published rituals breathed new life into them and they survived the Second World War, if only to dwindle slowly into legend. Perhaps it is as well that the old Order, exposed, dissected and catalogued, should now be put away as an historical curiosity and a chapter in the spiritual unfolding of Man.

I can only echo Regardie's sentiments as he expressed them to me in a letter written many years ago: 'I sometimes wish in moments of reverie, that Crowley, the O.T.O., Waite and the Golden Dawn would all gently blow away in a cloud and disappear and never be heard from again'.

Amen to that.

# Iŋdex of Naɱes

# Bibliography

CICERO, Chic & Sandra Tabatha *Self-Initiation into the Golden Dawn Tradition.* A Complete Curriculum of Study for both the Solitary Magician and the Working Magical Group. Llewellyn, 1995.

GILBERT, R. A. *The Golden Dawn, Twilight of the Magicians.* Aquarian 1983.

GILBERT, R. A. *The Golden Dawn Companion.* A Guide to the History, Structure and Workings of the Hermetic Order of the Golden Dawn. Aquarian, 1986.

HOWE, Ellic *The Magicians of the Golden Dawn.* A Documentary History of a Magical Order 1887–1923. Routledge & Kegan Paul, 1972. The definitive history of the Golden Dawn.

KING, Francis (Ed.) *Astral projection, Ritual Magic and Alchemy.* By S.L. Mathers and others. Hitherto Unpublished Golden Dawn Material. Second edition. Aquarian, 1987.

KUNTZ, Darcy (Ed.) *The Complete Golden Dawn Cipher Manuscript.* Deciphered, translated and edited. Holmes, 1996.

KUNTZ, Darcy (Ed.) *The Golden Dawn Source Book.* Edited, with an Introduction. Holmes, 1996.

REGARDIE, Israel *The Golden Dawn.* An account of the Teachings, Rites and Ceremonies of the Order of the Golden Dawn. Second edition, revised and enlarged. Llewellyn, 1969, 2 volumes.

An extensive bibliography of books and articles on the Golden Dawn has been published by Mr. Kuntz (Holmes, 1996). The manuscript archives of the Order are held in a number of private and institutional libraries. I have described them in some detail in my paper 'Magical Manuscripts: an Introduction to the Archives of the Hermetic Order of the Golden Dawn' (*Yeats Annual No. 5*, Edited by Warwick Gould. Macmillan, 1987). In preparing this book I have also made use of the extensive manuscript materials in the Yarker Library and the High Council Library of the S.R.I.A. To the trustees of the former and to the Librarian-General of the latter I am deeply indebted.